PERUVIAN
MYTHS AND LEGENDS

Compiled by Fernando Rosas

Translated by Mabel Borja
Special thanks to Saskia Tegels

 **Ediciones
El Lector**

© De la Presente Edición
Ediciones El Lector S.R.L.
San Francisco 221 Arequipa
Telefax: 054 288677
e-mail: el_lector69@hotmail.com

Diagramación y diseño de cubierta
Omar Suri

©Translated by Mabel Borja

Tiraje: 3000 ejemplares

Hecho el Depósito Legal 2005-8079
ISBN 9972-9706-3-9
Registro de Proyecto Editorial N.º 10401010500657

Impresión
Tarea Asociación Gráfica Educativa

Primera Edición

CONTENTS

Introduction 7

First Part

KON 15
PACHACAMAC 17
PACHACAMAC AND VICHAMA 19
WIRACOCHA 22
ILLAPA 25
TUNUPA 27
PARIACACA 29
CONOPAS 31
HUAYTACURY 32
MAMA RAYGUANA 35
THE CANARIS 36
PACHAMAMA 39
THE WACON MYTH 40
QAMIRAYA WIRACOCHA 42
URPAY HUACHAC 46
THE URPAY HUACHAC MYTH 48
THE HUANCAS 49
NAYLAMP AND THE LAMBAYEQUE CULTURE 52
THE AYAR BROTHERS AND THE INCA ORIGIN 54

Second Part

The Turtle 65
The Painted Huaca Of Illimo 67
The Yucal Legend 69
The Pachacamac Islands 70
The Santa Elena Giants 71
The Amarus 73
Warivilca 75
Pitusira 77
The Namla 79
The Alpamayo Princess 81
Animal War 83
Death of Three Pishtacos 88
The Pongo's Dream 93
The Fox and the Huaychao 99
The Mother of all Stones 101
The Yaku-mama 106
The Turtle and the Fox 108
The Heavens the Earth and the Hedgehog 110
The Trip to Heaven 112

Apendix

Peruvian Flora And Fauna 115

Glossary 123

Bibliography 129

INTRODUCTION

Some historical, archaelogical and ethnographic research reveal, that in Inca time, the Andean man was obsessed with tradition. He was attached to the acquired forms and filled with a fear of change. He longed to preserve the past and this longing was expressed in his customs and habits that later developed into institutions and practices through which he remembered his history. The Andean way of life was a constant reminder of the past. This is evident in the Pacarina Cult: The worshipping of places in nature, where the first ancestor of each clan, were said to have appeared. Also in the Malquis Cult: A mummy was treated as a live human being.

There is a theory that says: Andean people were specially enchanted by the past All their rites and customs, both private and public, were perpetual references to the past. Each Inca Emperor who died in Cuzco was embalmed and kept in his own palace surrounded by his possessions. Even after his passing, the Inca relatives attended him and and carried him to the main square for public events. The memory of his deeds was put into song and thus passed on to his descendants or Panaca. The Panaca was the Inca kinship group, equivalent to the nobility in a monarchy.

According to historic documents written by representatives of the Inquisition: Andeans mysteriously refused to abandon their hostile enviroment. We know now that the

7

reason for their resistance was due to the ancient practices of the Pacarina Cult. Examples of their attachment to their land and the birthplace of their ancestors are the stone and bronze models of their fields, which were kept safeguarded in their homes.

As we know, myths and legends precede history and the Incas were said to be rich in fables and legends. Garcilaso de la Vega wrote: " I remember having heard plenty of short stories in my youth." The Incas kept in such stories religious legends; famous deeds of their kings and leaders and moral doctrines. Garcilaso de la Vega's testimony, along with the legends and myths compiled by *cronistas* —first American historians— and the representatives of the Inquisition, confirm the Incas narrative vocation. The fact that in Quechua and Aymara, the main Andean languages, there are many words to express the verb "to narrate", is also seen as a confirmation of the importance story telling had in the Andean way of life.

The myth making epoch is seen by some as a poetic time and by others as a time of insanity. Finally there are those who highlight the importance of mythology in the process of piecing together the way of thinking of a particular society. In spite of the fact that myths take place at a time that never existed and that it has been said that they are the result of language misunderstandings, the psychology and ancient history of a society are discovered through its myths.

Although it is true that myths mix up past present and future, they also contain elements from real life and refer to events that took place in the remote past, which might coincide with forgotten cultural expressions. Archaeological discoveries have confirmed the relation between myths and ancient architecture and pottery. Mythology is also useful in the study of the genealogy of Gods and humans.

Myths are means of preserving and communicating attitudes, ideas, feelings and morals, not only about life and death, but community and social relations. In Inca mythology like in any other mythology real and imaginary facts take place in a fantasy world, but they always contain historical elements..

Inca myths are a mixture of horrifying tales of violence and destruction along with humorous and optimistic elements. We come across: Genesis stories; The war between God Kon and God Pachacamac; Wiracocha's creation of the first human beings, he even designed the different attire worn by each one of the primitive tribes; Legendary characters like Naylamp, Tonopa or Manco Capac who seem heroes from adventure stories. Other characters are punished for their arrogance or forbidden love by being transformed into islands or hills. Fights between lions, snakes or giants produce earthquakes, the Milky Way is a shining river, the constelation is seen as totemic animals; The stars are quinoa or maize grains spilled over from heavenly banquets, thunder and rain are produced by the punch of an angry God to a mainden's water pitcher, Chasca or Venus , the one with the tangled up hair is the Sun God'd favorite page, the *sacacas* or comets fly with their fire wings to hide on the highest snow peaks, Quilla; the moon, gives sweet advice on matters of jealousy and love.

Some might highlight the humorous element in Inca myths, even the universal drama of the deluge is made fun of by the ending, when the surviving couple floats inside a drum. The snake that crawls on the ground is suddenly transformed into the zig zag of lightening. The fox climbs to the moon thanks to a couple of ropes. Human beings come out of three eggs: Leaders come out of a golden egg; Chosen women come out of a silver egg and the serfs and worker come out of a copper egg. In a cinematographic version of the deluge the herdsmen who have taken refuge on the high peaks realize happily that the mountain grows as the water level increases and shrinks when the water level decreases.

The beginning of these stories might produce fear, but towards the end the fear is transformed into positive thinking and a general faith in human destiny.

The Inca Empire, like many other empires, ended up being lead by a war mongering aristocracy, who converted it into an expansionist and warring nation. Originally the Incas were an agricultural society and this is the reason why ancient legends celebrate the victory of men over a hostile terrain and praise the planting of seeds and the collection of crops. Wiracocha is the civilizing, protecting and giving God, who represents life and fertility. Mamacoca is another giving Goddess who comes down from the heavens and shelters under a coca bush, from then on coca leafes help human beings to allivate hunger and sadness.

The most popular Inca myths are those related to agriculture. The Ayar brothers and their wives come out of Pacaritampu or Down Inn, carrying their shining axes and their slings capable of bringing down whole mountains. They are looking for a predestined land where they want to plant potatoes and maize, the most nutritious and important crops of the Inca Empire. The names of the Ayar brothers refer to the discovery of some foodstufs. Ayar

Cachi: Salt; Ayar Ichu: Chili pepper; Ayar Auca: Roasted maize.

When God Wiracocha sends his children: Manco Capac and Mama Ocllo to found an Empire, they carry a magic Gold bar which will sink in the most fertile land, symbolizing the agrarian destiny of the Incas. On the other hand, the worst possible punishment for breaking divine law, in all Inca myths and legends, is to be transformed into a stone, a symbol of barrenness and infertility.

It has already being said that myths and legends are the poetic and popular forms which precede history.

FIRST
PART

Kon

Kon is one of the oldest Andean divinities. He was worshipped in the central and northern Peruvian Coast up to 300AD (Horizonte Temprano). Kon's cult was previous to Pachacamac. It is said that God Pachacamac defeated and sent God Kon into exile. Kon appears in genesis stories as the creator of the first human beings and is related to water in Andean mythology.

Kon's main temple was in the Chillon valley, north of Lima, as the priest and historian Villar Cordoba wrote in 1935. His memory still prevails in place names such as: Kon-Kon and Kon-kan on the Peruvian Coast

Kon was said to have a boneless body, was light agile and able to fly. He was supposed to move at great speed up mountains and down valleys.

Once invasions from the south took place the worship of Kon was substituted, throughout the coast, by the worship of Pachacamac.

God Kon was believed to have arrived to the coast from the mountain region of central Peru. On arrival he decided to create the first human beings and, to secure their comfortable survival, he created fertile valleys; many rivers and sent plenty of rain. Those fortunate people lived amongst abundance and comfort until they forgot about their creator. Their attitude made God Kon angry and to punish his people he turned the fertile lands into deserts and took away the rain. This is said to be the reason for the barren lands along the Peruvian coast. God Kon only left a few rivers and thus, in order to tend to their fields, his people had to work hard and build a complicated water system of long and winding aqueducts. Kon carried out his punishment in spite of people's prayers and sacrifices.

A god called Pachacamac appeared at around this time, he was said to be the child of the Sun and the Moon and wanted to take over Kon's place. Both gods confronted each other and their fight shook the whole world. In the end Kon, was defeated and sent into exile. The victorious Pachacamac transformed Kon's followers into cats, parrots and pumas and created new human beings along with the essential means for their survival. The inhabitants of the Peruvian coast today are supposedly the descendants of the people created by Pachacamac.

Pachacamac

Pachacamac was one of the most powerful and feared gods in Andean mythology. He was worshipped mainly on the coastal region of Peru, but there is evidence that his cult spread to the Andean and Amazon regions too. He was believed to be the creator of the universe; the god of tremors and master of oracles. He was also known as Pachacayochic (the one who makes the earth shake). He was greatly feared, taking into account that Peru is in an earthquake prone zone. It was said that the slightest movement of his head caused a tremor and that a change of position or a brusque movement caused a cataclysm.

Pachacamac's oracles had prestige all around the Inca Empire. People from all walks of life would travel great distances to consult it, including the powerful Cuzco rulers.

This god had many temples dedicated to him on the Peruvian coast. The most important one was built in the Lurin valley, south of Lima. Archaeological remains of this great worshipping site can still be visited. The Pachacamac cult which started between 300 and 700 AD (Intermedio Temprano), reached its climax between 700 and 1200 AD (Horizonte Medio) continued during the Inca period. At the time of the Spanish arrival the temple still received pilgrims from all over the Empire.

On January 1533 and after Inca Atahualpa's kidnapping, Hernando Pizarro, along with 23 other Spaniards went into Pachacamac's main temple in Lurin in order to take gold, silver and precious stones, as part of the rescue demanded for Atahualpa's release. Hernando Pizarro and his men burst into the inner chamber of the temple and found the wooden idol of this most feared god. The image was destroyed in front of the astonished and impotent temple guards and replaced by a cross. Spanish historians wrote at the time that the desperation of Pachacamac's worshippers was great, not because the destruction of the idol proved the fallacy of their beliefs, but because they were left unprotected against earthquakes.

Pachacamac and Vichama

Pachacamac created the first man and the first woman to inhabit the land, but he forgot to provide them with food, soon after the first man died of starvation. The heartbroken woman, having been left alone, complained bitterly to the Sun God: Why do you allow me to live on this Earth only to die of starvation?. Moved by the widow's cries the Sun God came down and with his powerful rays made her pregnant, four days later the woman gave birth to a son. Pachacamac realized what had happened and was filled with anger. He felt that the Sun God was taking over, and to avenge the offence he got hold of the child and taking no notice of the mother's pleads, killed him and tore his body into pieces. Then, he took the pieces and buried each one in a different site. After a while, out of the burried teeth grew maize; out of the burried bones grew yuca (cassava) and out of the burried flesh grew cucumbers and fruit. He did this to make sure human beings would always have crops and would never forget their God.

Everyone was happy thanks to the abundance of crops and all felt indebted to Pachacamac, except the mother of the dead child, who saw in each crop the image of her son.

Inspired by her maternal love and her desire for revenge, she begged the Sun God to punish the crime or at least provide some consolation for her pain. The Sun God, moved again by the woman's cries for help, decided to create another child out of the navel of the dead one. He named the new child Vichama.

Very happy once again, the mother looked after her child with great love and tenderness. Filled with pride, she saw how her child became a handsome and slender young man. Unfortunately, once Vichama grew up he decided to leave his mother and go traveling to see all his father's creation.

The revengeful Pachacamac, taking advantage of Vichama's absence, killed the lonely mother, divided her body into small pieces and fed them to condors and vultures. He kept her hair and bones and hid them by the seashore. Pachacamac then created new human beings and chose what authorities would rule over them.

When Vichama returned from his travels he heard the bad news of his mother's death. He patiently looked for and found his mother's bones and hair and returned her to life, then went looking for Pachacamac to challenge him to a fight. But Pachacamac had decided not to kill again and went into hiding next to the sea, where his main temple was built. Vichama looked in vain for Pachacamac. Eventually, filled with anger for having failed to find him, directed his anger towards the people and accused them of having remained passive while his mother was killed. No matter how much they apologized and begged his forgiveness Vichama asked his father the Sun God to punish them and they were all transformed into stones and their land was decimated.

The land looked so desolate and barren that Vichama's heart was touched. He regretted what had been done and decided to ask his father to create new human beings. The Sun God, having listened to Vichama, sent him three eggs: a gold one, a silver one and a copper one. The noble men and the leaders appeared from the golden egg. The wives of the noble men and the leaders appeared from the silver egg. The male and female villagers appeared from the copper egg. Thus they all populated the land.

Wiracocha

The Wiracocha cult

dates back to the Wari Empire between 700 and 1200 AC (Horizonte Medio). Most historians agree on the importance of Wiracocha in Andean mythology. We will mention a few: Luis E. Valcarcel wrote that he was also known as Apo Con Ticci Wiracocha Pachayachachic, which means the god of all creation. Guaman Poma de Ayala called the most ancient period in Andean history: Wari Wiracocha Runa.Sarmiento de Gamboa stated that the Ayar Brothers, who were the mythical founders of the Inca Empire, came out of the Pacaritambo mountain under the orders of Ticci Wiracocha. Franklin Pease wrote that Wiracocha follows the sun's movements and after having to put order into the world goes to inhabit his confines. Unlike his colleagues, Franklin Pease does not see him as the creator.

The Wiracocha cult thrives specially in the Southern Andes over the first decades of the Inca Empire , so much so, that the eighth Inca Emperor was called Wiracocha Inca. It was not until the reign of Pachacutec and the beginning of his expansionist period, that the Wiracocha cult was replaced by the Sun cult. As it is known, the Inca

Emperors believed they were direct descendants of Inti the Sun God. There is archaeological evidence that most Wiracocha temples, including the main one in San Pedro de Cacha, Cuzco, disappeared during Pachacutec's reign.

It has to be mentioned that there is strong biblical influence in the "cronicas" —the writings of the first American historians (cronistas)—. " Wiracocha was a man of medium height, dressed in a white robe, who carried a sceptre and a book in his hands". Sarmiento de Gamboa.

Most early writers agreed that Wiracocha appeared in the beginning of time in a place called Tiahuanaco, on the shores of lake Titicaca. Having decided to populate the earth, he sculpted large statues in stone, which were deformed and did not look like human beings. When the god looked at his creation he was disappointed. "It is not right to make creatures this tall" he said. He destroyed them and created new human beings, inspired by his own image.

The sequence of his creation was as follows: deep inside the earth Wiracocha sculpted stone statues of men and women. He placed them in different openings to the outside world like caves, lakes and water springs and he named these places *Pacarinas*. He then named each statue and by naming them, gave them life and the statues became human beings. To create animals, Wiracocha went through the same process. The sun, the moon and the stars had not been created yet, thus darkness prevailed.

Wiracocha ordered human beings to live in peace, unity and virtue, but they forgot and became corrupt. Angry for having been disobeyed, he converted them back into stone and unleashed a deluge.

Once the deluge was over, he created new human beings and in order for them not to get lost in the dark, created the sun, the moon and the stars and placed them in the sky.

The god, having finished his creation, left Tiahuanaco and went north. He was followed by his two assistants: Imamana Wiracocha and Tocapu Wiracocha. He then ordered Tocapu to go to the Coast and Imamana to go to the Amazon, while he travelled to the Andes. His assistants were told to create plants, animals and people through their path.

When Wiracocha arrived to a village called Cacha he found out that the villagers had forgotten their creator. They humiliated him and even tried to kill him. Outraged by the behavior of such ungrateful people, the god decided to punish them. He made fire fall from the heavens, burning plants, animals and the soil itself. Filled with tribulation and repentance, the villagers begged Wiracocha to have pity on them. He felt compassion, forgave them and stopped the fire.

Wiracocha reached the end of his journey when he arrived to Puerto Viento and Manta, on what is now the coast of Ecuador. It was there where he met up with his two assistants: Imamana and Tocapu. God Wiracocha, before leaving for good, revealed the future to his people and promised to send prophets who would teach and protect them. The god and his assistants then went towards the sea, walked on the water and disappeared in the horizon. Wiracocha means sea froth in Quechua, the Inca language.

Illapa

Illapa the god of lightning, was one of the most important and feared gods of the pre-hispanic pantheon. He was worshipped throughout the Andean region and his image was placed next to the Sun God and Ticci Wiracocha in the Coricancha temple*.

Illapa was the god of rain, hail, thunder and landslides. These were essential elements for the agrarian Andean population, who inhabited a region plagued by drought. Thus, Illapa's power was often called upon to send rain or keep hail away from crops.

Illapa's main festival took place in the month of May and entailed animal and human sacrifices. Offerings of food, coca leaves and beer were made to the fire. During this festival Andeans were expected to eliminate salt from their diet and abstain from sexual activity.

It was believed that Illapa was living in the heavens, armed with a sling and a club. Although his main temple was located in Pucamarca, Illapa was known in different places by different names, some of which were: Catequil, Libia, Chuquilla, Catiulla, and Intiyllapa.

After the Spanish conquest, catholic priests found it particularly difficult to eradicate the beliefs and practices

---

* The main Inca Temple in Cuzco

of the Illapa cult. However, Illapa was eventually substituted in the Andean cosmogony by Santiago the catholic apostle. In the sixteeth century, it was believed that the sounds of thunder in the heavens were made by Santiago's galloping horse.

Tunupa

Tunupa or Tonopa was an Andean god whose cult dates back to before the Wiracocha cult. He was worshipped mainly on the highland planes known as the Altiplano and also on the southern coast of Peru, in the north of Chile and a region of Bolivia called Collasuyo during the Inca Empire. There is still a lake in Arequipa and a volcano in Oruro that are named after God Tunupa.

This mighty god was said to exercise control over lightning, volcanoes, rain, rivers and water springs. His rays fertilized the soil and when they fell on lake Titicaca impregnated the fish.

Tunupa was replaced by Wiracocha during the Inca Empire and his atributes were taken by Saint Thomas the apostle during the Spanish colony. To this day he is represented by a preacher with long hair and beard.

The myth goes as follows: A long time ago a medium built man with long hair and beard arrived from the eastern region (what is now Paraguay). His name was Tunupa which means wise man or master.

The god travelled around the Collao region preaching tirelessly, until he arrived in a village called Yanquesupa, where the villagers insulted him and threw him out. Tunupa cursed the village and flooded it, as a punishment. It is said that that is how lake Yanquesupacocha appeared.

His wanderings took him to a village on top of a very high mountain called Cachapucara, there he found the idol of a female god. The finding made him so angry that he made fire fall upon the village, which was detroyed along with the entire mountain.

When Tunupa arrived at Quenamari, the villagers were celebrating a wedding with a feast. The god started preaching using sweet and loving words, but no one paid any attention. Possessed by fury, Tunupa turned the whole population into stones.

Wandering through the Carabaya area Tunupa was said to have made a cross, carried it on his shoulders and placed it at the top of a mountain called Carabuco. The confused inhabitants, tied him, took him prisoner and condemned him to death. Tunupa miraculously escaped and went to lake Titicaca. Stretching out his arms, he travelled at great speed across the water. He rested on a large rock in the middle of the lake and arrived at a place on the shores called Tiahuanaco. There he turned everyone into stone, as nobody listened to his preachings either. Finally, through the Cachamarca river, Tunupa arrived to the sea and disappeared in the water.

Pariacaca

The followers of God Pariacaca were mainly on the highlands and coastal areas of central Peru. He was the god of lightning, rain and landslides. He lived on the snow-capped mountain called Anan Pariacaca, where his main temple was built. Many pilgrims visited the temple to consult the oracle. In order to reach it, pilgrims had to climb steep steps carved on the rock, Pariacaca's temple continued to receive pilgrims until the end of the sixteen century, when catholic priests violently eradicated the cult. Francisco de Avila and a group of Jesuits climbed up to the temple and destroyed it along with Pariacaca's idol. They also destroyed God Xamuna's idol which was worshipped in the same temple. Finally the priests placed a cross where Pariacaca's idol had been. When the missionaries returned to the village of San Lorenzo de Quinti they found the villagers carrying lighted torches, looking very distressed and crying inconsolably: "Pariacaca is dead".

It is said, that a long time ago God Huallallo Carhuincho lived in the Andean area the Incas called Huancas. His abode was a snow-capped mountain peak and people believed he sent thunder, lightening, rain and hail to remind them of his presence. He was said to procure grass to feed the herds and water for plentiful crops, but in contrast he also sent illnesses to men and animals alike. God Huallallo Carhuincho was therefore greatly feared by his followers and received plenty of human sacrifices as offerings. At around this time, five eggs appeared on the Condorcota mountain and out of one of them came God Pariacaca. He acquired human form and along with his four brothers went to live on the highest Andean peaks, that is where God Huallallo Carhuincho also lived.

Francisco de Avila wrote in the Huarochiri Manuscripts (1598) that it was believed a great fight took place between the gods. Pariacaca and his brothers attacked from five different places, first with red and yellow rain and later with lightning. Huallallo Carhuincho transformed himself into a fire, so big that its flames reached the sky. The water from Pariacaca's rain went down towards the sea and on the way formed a lake called Mullucocha. This was only the beginning. Pariacaca and his brothers continued relentlessly to send lightning and hail until Huallallo Carhuincho was defeated and fled to the Antisuyo region. Thus the victorious Pariacaca became the god of the area.

Conopas

Conopas are deities who protect nature and crops. Each edible plant has a protector or Conopa who ensures the plant produces good and plentiful fruits. Conopas are represented by small statues made with great care and accuracy, specially with regards to colour and form. Nevertheless, sometimes certain features are exaggerated, such as: a corn cob with extra large grains or two corn cobs coming out of one stalk. These statues are buried in fields or placed in barns or food storage places.

Animal Conopas are called Illas and are miniature statues of domestic animals. Farmers ritually offer the Canopas first to their gods and only after they bury them in their fields or farm yards to make sure their animals breed and their crops are abundant.

The best known Conopas are: Mama Sara the corn protector; Mama Papa the potato protector; Mama Uchu the aji (hot pepper) protector; Mama Coca the coca plant protector and Huasi Camac the home protector.

To this day the name Conopa is also given to small stones, found in nature, but shaped in the form of animals or people. These are considered to be life protecting amulets.

31

Huaytacuri

In ancient times, there was a poor man by the name of Huaytacuri who lived in a small hut and only had potatoes for food. However, rumour had it that he was the son of God Pariacaca.

Around the same time, in the town of Anchicocha, lived a rich and powerful man call Tantañamca who was loved and respected for his wisdom. One day, he fell terribly ill and in spite of being seen by the best doctors, no one could explain the cause of his illness.

Huaytacuri went for a walk, and all of a sudden he felt very sleepy and decided to take a nap by the roadside. Very near there two foxes were chatting away, exchanging news. One of them was telling the other about the rich man in Anchicocha who had fallen terribly ill and explained that the reason no one had found a cure for his illness was because the illness was caused by his wife's infidelity.

Having overheard the foxes talk, Huaytacuri went to visit Tantañamca and promised to cure him if he gave Huaytacuri one of his daughters for a wife. Tantañamca had two daughters, the eldest was married to a rich man and the youngest, Chaupiñamca, still unwed.

When Huaytacuri told Tantañamca the cause of his illness, he was cured. True to his word, Tantañamca gave his young and beautiful daughter to be married. Everyone was happy with the arrangement except Chaupiñamca's brother-in-law, who was outraged that this beautiful young girl would marry a poor, potatoe eater. The brother-in-law, filled with anger, decided to challenge the groom to a contest that would last for days.

The first day, the bother-in-law told Huaytacuri, "tomorrow I'll challenge you to a singing and drinking contest." Huaytacuri accepted and immediately went to consult his father God Pariacaca. Pariacaca advised him: "Go to the mountain, lay on the floor and pretend to be a dead "huanco" In the morning, two foxes will appear and bring with them a drum and a drinking container. When they place these two objects on the floor and are about to eat you, grab the objects and run away" Huaytacuri did exactly as he was told and later went to see the brother in law with the magic drum and drinking container in hand.

The singing competition began with the brother-in-law singing and dancing with all the women invited. Two hundred songs later, it was Huaytacuri's turn. Huaytacuri began to sing accompanied by his magic drum and to everyone's surprise, the earth and the hills began to move. Huaytacuri was declared the unquestionable winner.

The second competition began inmediatly after. The brother-in-law presented hundreds of bowls of beer to the guests who drank until it was finished. Huaytacuri only brought with him his magic drinking container. Everyone laughed at him and asked: "How do you expect to quench everyone's thirst with just one drinking container?" but to their amazement, Huaytacuri filled their bowls multiple times until they were all drunk. Huataycuri was declared the winner again.

The brother-in-law challenged Huaytacuri to five more competitions and he was defeated in all of them. Overcome by shame and embarrassment the brother-in-law fled to the mountains where he was transformed into a deer. His wife fled to the coast where she turned into stone.

Mama Rayguana

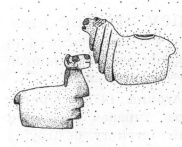

A long time ago, when the land was barren and many died of starvation, people decided to ask a bird called a chihuanco for help. The chihuanco or zorzal has yellow beak and legs. Having listened to the starving, the chihuanco, along with other birds, elaborated a plan to help them.

According to plan, a humming bird threw a handful of flies on the eyes of Goddess Rayguana. When the goddess desperately tried to get rid of them, she unintentionally let go of her young son Conopa. Swiftly, an eagle got hold of the child and kidnapped him, promising to give him back only if the Goddess provided the starving people with food.

Desperate to recover her son, Goddess Rayguana gave maize, quinoa, potatoes and other Andean root vegetables like ollucos, mashhuas and ocas to the people who lived in the Andes and sweet potatoes and beans to the ones who lived by the coast. That was supposed to be the beginning of agriculture in the area.

To these days, farmers bury small statues called Conopas in their fields, in the hope that Mama Rayguana will provide them with plentiful crops.

The Canaris

They are the legendary warriors who lived in Canaribamba, near Quito in the Northern Andes.

Around 1470 Emperor Tupac Yupanqui conquered their territory destroying Guapnodeling, the capital city. Emperor Huayna Capac later built Ingapirca near the site where the old capital had been.

The brave Canaris, once defeated, became part of the Inca army. As we know, the Incas' policy towards their defeated enemies was one of association rather than enslavement.

During the civil war led by the brothers Huascar and Atahualpa, the Canaris took side with Atahualpa. Nevertheless, when the Spanish arrived they took side with the conquerors and fought along them during the long years of the conquest. They also fought against Manco Inca during his uprising and when Tupac Amaru, the last Inca, was defeated in Vilcabamba in 1572 a Canari warrior was chosen to behead him.

The Spanish rewarded the Canaris for their help by giving them special privileges and favours. The case of Martin Chilche is an example, he was a Canari and was the highest authority in the Yucay Valley near Cuzco, until his death.

The Canaris myth starts with a great deluge in the north Andes, what is now Ecuador. There were only two survivors, they were brothers who had taken refuge at the top of the Huanynan mountain. Once the rain subsided and pressed by hunger, they left their refuge to go looking for fruits and roots to eat. One day, as they returned to their refuge, tired and sad because they had not got enough food, they found their table served with delicacies and drinks. Once they recovered from their surprise they sat at the table and ate and drunk until they had had plenty.

The same mysterious happening occurred over the next twelve days. Unable to contain their curiosity by then, they decided to find out who their benefactor was. They conceived a plan: while one of them went hunting and gathering, the other would remain waiting and hide to discover who came in and brought the delicacies. Hours later, the brother who stayed in, saw two female huacamayos (type of parrot with long tail and colourful feathers) come in, transform themselves into two beautiful women and got on to prepare the food. The young man came out of his hiding place to greet them, but the frightened women inmediately converted back into huacamayos and fled.

When the second brother returned and found out what had happened, they decided that both would stay in the next day. Nothing happened for the next two days, but on the third day the two huacamayos appered, transformed themselves into women and started cooking. The two brother then came out of their hiding places, closed the door swiftly and got hold of the women. The women screamed and tried to escape, but the brothers calmed them down with loving words and caresses. Then they asked what the reason was for their generosity. The women responded that Ticci Wiracocha had sent them so the brothers would not starve. The two brothers married the women and had many children. That is supposed to be the origin of the Canaris.

The Canaris worship the Huanynam mountain as their Apu (mountain god) as well as the huacamayos, to this day huacamayo feathers are considered sacred.

Pachamama

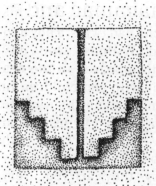

Pachamama means mother Earth. She is still worshipped in the Andes. She is the goddess of fertility and the provider of food for animals and human beings, she is also seen as the house protector.

The planting season in the Andes is in August and it is during this month when Pachamama receives most offerings. Farmers offer her chicha (corn beer), coca leaves, lard or ghee, etc. to make sure they attain good crops.

Chicha has always had an important role in Andean rituals. Andeans believe that the Pachamama feels thirst like any human being and this is the reason why they spill some chicha on the ground when they have a drink. They do not want to offend her by not sharing their drink. They still fear her punishment.

Offerings are also given to Pachamama at the time of building a house. She is said to protect houses from thieves, illnesses and ghosts.

Catholic priests tried to transfer the Pachamama's cult to the Virgin Mary. After the Spanish arrival Goddess Pachamama is sometimes known as "Pachamama Santa Tierra" (Pachamama St. Earth).

The Wacon Myth

God Pachacamac and his wife Pachamama had twins, a boy and a girl called Willcas. One day Pachacamac disappeared in the sea abandoning his wife and children in the fog. Lost and not knowing what to do Pachamama and her twins walked towards a far away light. Their path was besieged by monsters and hungry beasts. Finally they arrived, very frightened, to the cave where the light came from. Inside the cave was Wacon, a demon who looked as horrid as he was fierce. He greeted them "Come in, don't be frightened, take a seat while I cook". Wacon stared at Pachamama while he cooked potatoes in a stone pot. To get rid of the children, he sent them for water to a far away fountain. Then he tried to seduce Pachamama, but failed. This made him very angry and he ended up killing her and eating her whole body.

When the children returned with the water and asked for their mother Wacon told them she had gone out, but that she would return soon. The twins waited in vain and after a few days they became very upset and would not stop crying because they missed their mother. Fortunately, a bird called "Huay-Chua" felt pity for the Willcas, told them what had happened to their mother and advised them to run away.

When Wacon was not paying attention, the Willcas escaped from the cave and run as fast as they could. Many animals helped the twins as they fled, specially a young female fox, who adopted them and hid them in her den.

Wacon was furious when he discovered the escape, so he looked for the children everywhere and asked many animals about their whereabouts, but they gave him wrong leads and fooled him. While he continued his search he came across the young female fox and asked her if she had seen the twins. She told him: "Yes, I have seen them, they went down that path over there, if you want to find them, go to the top of this mountain and call them pretending you are their mother".

The demon went up the mountain, without suspecting that the fox had prepared a trap. When he reached the top, he fell in the trap and fell into a deep ravine. His fatal fall produced a great earthquake.

Thus the Willcas were saved from the demon who had murdered their mother and stayed to live with the fox, who looked after them as if they were her kin. One day, God Pachacamac, the twins' father felt pity for them, sent down two pieces of rope and ordered them to climb up to the sky. When they got to the sky, Pachacamac turned the male Willca into the sun and the female Willca into the moon. So the twins continued to wander in the sky, as they had with their mother on Earth. Pachamama became the snow-capped mountain called, to this day: the Widow.

Qamiraya Wiracocha

Early Andean historians divided time before the Spanish arrival into four different periods, each defined by a different god. The first era is defined by God Yanañamca Tutañamca; the second by God Huallallo Carhuincho; the third by God Pariacaca and the fourth era by Cuniriya Wiracocha, also known as Qamiraya.

It is believed that Qamiraya decided to come down to the area of Central Peru, dressed as an old beggar. During his travels he was made fun of and laughed at because of his appearance. A beautiful girl called Q'awiraya lived in the area. She lived alone and kept to herself and did not allow any man to get near her. Many wise men wanted to marry her but she rejected them all. She spent her time knitting under the shade of a lucuma (variety of eggfruit) tree.

God Qamiraya fell passionately in love with the girl and decided to use all his powers to make her his wife; taking the form of a sparrow he flew to the lucuma tree and sang:

> *News, news, beautiful woman*
> *News, news lonely woman*
> *You will conceive a child, you will conceive a boy*

Upon hearing the bird's song, Q'awiraya responded:

Bad omen sparrow
Who makes fun of me saying
You will conceive a child, you will conceive a boy
it is you who will have offspring

As she spoke she threw stones at the sparrow. God Qamiraya then, using his wisdom, decided to place his semen on the ripest fruit. When the fruit fell on the floor Q'awirawa picked it up and ate it, instantly she became pregnant. Nine months later she gave birth to a boy who she breastfed for a year. She asked her sisters who the father of her child could be and how had she conceived a child, but they did not know the answer. In her quest she decided to invite all the wise men of the village. They all showed up dressed in their best clothes hoping to atract Q'awiraya. She asked each one of them, but they all denied being the father of her child.

When the time came to ask Qamiraya, still looking like a beggar, she thought "this man could not possibly be the father" so she did not even bother to ask him.

Unable to find the answer to her question, she asked her son to identify his own father. She told the elders: "the one whose lap the child chooses to climb up, to will be the father"

The child crawled in front of the men and did not go near any of them, but when he was in front of Qamiraya, his little face lit up and climbed on to his lap.

The distressed woman screamed: "How could I possibly have a beggar's child?". She then picked up her son and ran away towards the sea.

God Qamiraya pulled off his rags and making his gold suit become apparent, ran after the girl shouting: Sister Q'awiraya, look at me, I am dressed in gold, I am not a beggar.

Q'awiraya, without turning back, jumped into the sea with her son and they were instantly transformed into two rocks.

God Qamiraya continued looking for her, on his way he met a condor and asked: Have you come across Q'awiraya? and the condor answered: Yes, not far from here, you will catch up with her soon.

God Qamiraya gratefully said: You will live longer than most animals, you will eat guanaco and vicuña meat. Whoever kills you will also die.

Qamiraya later came across a skunk and asked: Have you seen Q'amirawa? and the skunk answered: She is too far away, you will never find her.

Qamiraya was very upset and damned the skunk.: You will only walk at night and you will smell so badly that you will be hated.

Later, he came across a puma and asked the same question and the puma replied: She is walking nearby. You will reach her shortly.

Qamiraya thanked the puma and said: Everyone will love you and you will eat llama meat. After your death, people will wear your skin on festive days and they will sacrifice many llamas in your honour.

He then came across a fox and in answer to his question the fox said it had not seen anyone.

Qamiraya damned the fox: People will hate you and consider you a bad omen. After they kill you they will throw your carcus as far away as possible.

Near by he met a sparrow hawk and asked about Q'awiraya. The sparrow hawk said: She is very close, you are about to find her.

Qamiraya told the sparrow hawk: You will be happy, and you will eat poultry and locals will place your body on their heads as a beautiful hat.

Then, Qamiraya met a flock of parrots, they told him: The woman with the baby in her arms is very far away, you will never find her.

Qamiraya dammed them: You will live in misery, will go hungry and people will hate you.

Qamiraya finally arrived at Pachakamiri's house, who at the time had two daughters. The girls were alone because their mother had gone to the sea shore to visit Q'awiraya.

When God Qamiraya found out that Pachakamiri's wife had gone to visit Q'awiraya, he got into a fury and threw into the sea all the fish Pachakamiri's wife kept in a pond. This is how the sea came to have fish.

Pachakanmiri's wife found out that God Qamiraya had tried to seduce her younger daughter and planned to throw him into the sea from the highest cliff. To carry out her plan she offered to delouse him at the top of the cliff, but he became suspicious and went so far away that no one saw him ever again.

Urpay Huachac

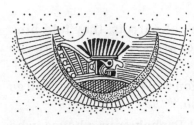 **She is an** ancient coastal divinity, her origins go back to the times when fishing started. Goddess Urpay Huachac was said to have a pond where she kept fish in the Pachacamac temple compound. This was interpreted to mean that fishing on the coast started in the ponds and small lakes by the seashore. Sea fishing started later, when Andean people brought reed boats to the coast along with the Qamiraya Cult.

Urpay Huachac was one of Pachacamac's wives and was the mother of the fish and the seagulls, she was worshipped in the area between the Chancay Valley in the north and Pisco in the south.

—The *cronista* Bernabe Cobo (1653) wrote that there was a fish farm in the Pachacamac temple compound, near the Mamaconas' palace.

—Maria Rostorowski wrote in 1973 that she had discovered in some Chancay pottery, images of Urpay Huachac next to fish and birds.

During the Colonial period, Magdalena's fishermen in Pisco worshipped the sea and hoping to catch abundant fish they would sometimes put bird wings in their nets. They called them Cusi.

Thanks to fish trading in the Andes, the Goddess' cult

expanded to the highlands. She was worshipped along with her son Auca Atama in Cajatambo and in Yauyos she was worshipped as God Pariacaca's sister.

Urpay Huachay's idols were replaced by the images of Saint Peter and Saint Paul, patrons of all fishermen.

The Urpay
Huachac Myth

As Pachacamac's wife, the Goddess lived happily together with her two daughters. Until one day God Cuniraya Wiracocha, also know as Camiraya, arrived and taking advantage of Pachacamac's absence tried to seduce Urpay Huachac and her daughters. To protect her daughters the Goddess transformed them into doves who flew away towards the horizon.

Urpay Huachac, to escape from Cuniraya Wiracocha, went into the sea and disappeared in the water. The God, frustrated and furious went into Pachacamac Temple, walked to Urpay Huachac's fish pond, destroyed it and threw the fish into the sea. To his surprise, once in the sea the fish reproduced rapidly and filled it with many types of fish.

The fishermen were so happy that they decided to worship Urpay Huachac as the Goddess of fish and birds.

The Huancas

The Huancas had their habitat around the provinces of Jauja, Concepcion and Huancayo. They emerged after the decline of the Huari Empire. Their Pacarina is called Huari Huillca, supposedly sixty Ayllus (Andean kinship groups) came out of it and gave origin to the Huanca nation. They grew crops in the valleys and they also had heards of llamas and alpacas in the highlands. They were known as a warrior nation. Their villages were built on mountain tops and were fortress towns. Their great capital, for over five hundred years was Siquillapucara and it is said to have had 15,000 inhabitants at one time.

In 1460 Inca Tupac Yupanqui and his army invaded Huanca territory, but it took them many months to enter. They lay siege to the Huanca capital, but Siquillapucara inhabitants resisted bravely, until they had to surrender due to hunger and thirst. The victorious Incas exiled the Huanca soldiers to far away lands and destroyed their capital.

The Huanca territory was incorporated into the Inca Empire, but the Huancas never accepted to be part of that Empire. A hidden hatred of the invaders persisted which became obvious during the Spanish Conquest, when the

Huancas took sides with the Spanish. The historian Waldemar Espinoza Soriano believes that the Huancas's alliance with the Spanish was crucial for the conquest of the Inca Empire.

The Huancas were known to eat dogs and were called Allcomicoc (dog eater in Quechua) by their neighbours. Their God was Huallallo Carhuincho. It is said that to celebrate a victory Huallallo Carhuincho ordered five dogs to be sacrificed and presented their meat and blood to his soldiers, who ate them along with some chicha (maize beer). The God later made wind instruments out of the dogs' skulls which produced a terrifying sound.

From then on the Huancas were attached to their dogs. They had them as companions; as sheep dogs; to keep birds away from their crops; to blow the cinders of their fires; to announce earthquakes; etc. They also taught them tricks and dances for entertainment. During their festivals they painted them and hanged turquoise necklaces and bracelets on them and sacrificed them to God Wiracocha, to God Wallallo Carhuicho and to their dead.

When Huancas died they were always buried with a dog. They believed the dog would carry water and accompany them on their journey ,which they said, run along unknown paths covered in gravel and without shade from trees.

The God of the Huancas, Wallallo Carhuincho, had defeated God Yanamka Tutamñaca. Wallallo Carhuincho had taken away fertile lands and had given them to the Huancas. God Yanamka's army officers never accepted their defeat and organized their army for a rebellion.

God Wallallo Carhuincho found out about the rebels' plans and went to the Quinancaya plane to watch them. The God realized that the enemies' arms were superior to the Huancas' and feared his people's defeat. Thus, without wasting any time sent the rebels a hail storm which lasted for five days. He also sent heavy rain and made red soil fall from the sky and to finish them off, he sent thunder and lightning. When the storm endes, the God was surprised to see that all the rebel officers were still alive. In a fury, stretched his arms to the sky and converted them into dogs.

Yanamka's officers started screaming and as they became dogs their screams sounded like howls. Annoyed by the noise, God Wallallo Carhuincho sent a huge lightning that made the whole earth shake and dogs to become mute. From then on the Huanca dogs have a hoarse and reluctant bark, although they are loyal and great companions in life and death.

Naylamp and the Lambayeque Culture

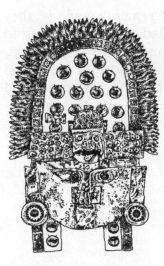

Naylamp was the Lambayeques' God of Water, they lived in the north Coast of Peru between 700 and 1350 AD. They were accomplished blacksmiths whose work had great artistic and technical value. They acquired great fame for their ceremonial knives (Tumis) and for their funeral masks.

Naylamp was represented in their pottery, metal work and their Tumis. The eyes of the God were slanted upwards and shaped rather like wings, he had a prominent nose and pointed ears with big earrings. His mouth is represented by a line and sometimes he carries a semi circular headdress. Naylamp, like Manco Capac, is a mythical and historic character as other dynasty founders were. Naylamp was said to have appeared at the Lambayeque coast in front of a large fleet. He had a huge entourage of soldiers, women and servants.

God Naylamp appeared with many wives, the name of his main wife was Ceterni. Among his personal servants were: Pitazoft his official trumpet player; Ninacola who was in charge of his bearers; Ninagintue who was in charge of drinks and beverages; Fongasidge who would cover the God's path with shell dust; Ochocalo who was his main cook; Xammuchec who was in charge of his make up; Ollopcppoc who was the God's bather and Llapchiluli who knitted his garments. The fleet arrived at the mouth of the Faquisllanga river, going in land they arrived at a beautiful and fertile valley where they built palaces and the Chot temple, where the idol of God Naylamp, carved in green stone, was placed. Naylamp was also called "Yampallec" the word Lambayeque derived from this name.

Naylamp reign lasted many years and during his kingdom the Lambayeques had peace and prosperity. When he died, it is said, he grew wings on his shoulders and flew to the sky. Naylamp's dynasty had twelve Kings, the last one was called Fempellec, who was bewitched by a beautiful woman and brought the decline of the Kingdom along with poverty and unhappiness, until it was conquered by Chimocapac and became part of the Chimu Empire.

The Ayar Brothers and the Inca Origin

There are many versions as to what happened between God Viracocha's creation and the beginning of the Inca Empire. It is known that the land was inhabited by Incas, but they were not organized into a nation state with laws, elected leaders nor a tax system. They all lived in small groups situated randomly, it is said that everyone was their own master and owner of a small field. When problems occurred they organized ad-hoc militias for their defence.

When a group was threatened by another group, they designated two leaders, one from their own group and another one from a different group. The latter was probably known for his bravery in the battle field. Sometimes a man of such characteristics would volunteer to fight on their side and organize their defence. People would obbey and follow their commands while the war lasted, but once the war was over, both leaders would cease to have power over the rest of the inhabitants and neither would receive payment of any kind. War leaders were called "cinche" which means brave.

The Cuzco valley has been populated since ancientti-

nes due to its fertile soil. It was inhabited by three different groups: Sauaserass, Antasayas and Guallas. The three
groups farmed the land peacefully over many centuries.

Six leagues south-east of Cuzco there is a place called
Paccari Tampu which means production place. In it there
is a hill called Tampu Tocco (Window's House) because it
has three windows: Maras Tocco; Sutic Tocco and the
middle one Capac Tocco (Rich Window) which was said to
be covered in gold.

The ethnic group called Maras came out of Maras Tocco
and they still live in Cuzco. The Tambos, who still live
around the hill, came out of Sutic Tocco. From Capac
Tocco, the main window, came out four brothers and four
sisters who said they came from the same place as Ticci
Viracocha and that the God had created them to be obeyed.
They adopted the surname Capac which later on was used
to name their first Inca (King).

The eight brothers and sisters declared: "We are strong
and wise and we will gather people around us and will be
powerful. We shall look for fertile lands and where ever we
find them we shall conquer the inhabitants and take away
their land. We shall unleash war on all those who do not
accept our authority." Mama Huaco and Manco Capac
were the most fierce and cruel and became the leaders.
The other brothers and sisters agreed with their plan.
They made people from the villages around the hill follow
them, promising to give them the wealth and the land of
any of the villages they would conquer and subjugate. That
is how the different ayllus (clans) went looking for people
and land to conquer, aiming mainly at peaceful people.

They departed taking arms and provisions following
their leaders. Manco Capac took with him, in a straw cage,

a falcon named Inti. They all worshipped it, some believed it was sacred, others that it was magic, but they all believed it would make Manco Capac powerful and make people follow him. The falcon was later left to his son as inheritance and passed on from one Inca to the next, all the way down to Inca Yupanqui. Manco Capac also carried with him a golden stick which he would plunge into the soil, to test it whenever they reached new lands.

They all arrived to a place, four leagues from the Cuzco Valley, called Guanacancha, where they stayed for a while and planted some fields. It was at this place where Manco Capac and Mama Ocllo married and she became pregnant. After a while Guanacancha did not seem fertile enough, so they moved on to a place called Tamboquiro, where Mama Ocllo gave birth to a son, who they named Sinchi Roca.

They were not pleased with the soil in Tamboquiro either, so they moved a quarter of a league away to a place called Huaysquisro. It was there where the brothers held a meeting to discuss their journey and how to get rid off Ayar Cachi, who was fierce, very strong and skilful with the sling and who had been very cruel to the inhabitants of the conquered areas. Sometimes he even attacked their own people. They were worried that their followers would abandon them bacause of Ayar Cachi's bad deeds.

Manco Capac worked out a plan to get rid off Ayar Cache and all the other brothers agreed to it. They called Ayar Cachi and told him: "Dear brother, we have left our gold goblets (topacusi), some seeds and our banner (napa) behind in Capac Tocco. For the good of us all, you will have to go and bring them back."

Ayar Cache refused to go back, but his sister Mama Huaco confronted and scolded him: "How can such a strong man like you be such a coward? Get ready for the journey, do not hesitate to go back to Tampu Tocco and do as you are told". Humilliated by these words, Ayar Cache left to obey the command. They all had decided to send Tambochacay to accompany Ayar Cache in his journey. Once they arrived to Tampu Tocco, Tambochacay had the instruction to murder Ayar Cache and return by himself.

Eventually they reached Tampu Tocco, on arrival Ayar Cache went in Capac Tocco Window in order to fetch the things his brothers had asked him to. Once Ayar Cache was inside, Tambochacay hurried to move a large stone, placed it in front of the window and sat on it, hoping Ayar Cache would remain inside and eventually die. When Ayar Cache returned to the window and found it blocked he realized he had been betrayed. There and then he decided to take revange on Tambochacay. He used all his strenght to push the stone out of the way and gave such loud screams that the whole mountain shook, but it was all in vain. Convinced of his imminent death he cursed Tambochacay: "Traitor! You, who have caused me so much harm, can forget about going back with the news of my death. It will never happen, because of your treacherous deed you will remain out there, transformed into a stone." That is what happened and to this day one can see the stone in front of Capac Tocco Window.

Once they heard about Ayar Cache's death, the seven brothers, who were still in Huaysquisro, regreted it. They cried his death bitterly, knowing his presence would be greatly missed at war. He was so skilful with the sling that with one throw he would make a mountain collapse and with another he would open a gorge. It is believed that the ravines and canyons in the area were made by Ayar Cache's sling.

The seven brothers and their followers left

Huaysquisro and arrived to Quirirmanta, at the slopes of a mountain which was later called Guanacauri. They had another meeting in this place and decided to share duties and resposibilities for the rest of the journey. It was agreed that Manco Capac who had married his sister Mama Ocllo should have more offspring to ensure the continuity of their line of descent, they also elected Manco Capac as their king or Ayar Ucho was chosen to be worshipped as Huaca and Ayar Auca would be the one to take possession of any new territories they conquer.

They continued their journey after the meeting and arrived at a mountain two leagues away from Cuzco, as they climbed up they saw a rainbow (guanacauri). Manco Capac interpreted it as a good omen and said: "This means that the world will not be destroyed by floods again. We shall climb to the top and from the top we shall choose where to settle our people." They came across an altar with an idol (Huaca) before they reached the top. The brothers agreed that it should be got rid off and sent Ayar Uchu to do the job. Once he was in front of the Huaca, and getting hold of all his courage he asked: "What are you doing here?." The Huaca then turned its head and looked at him. Ayar Ichu, at that very moment, felt transformed and told his brothers: "You have harmed me by sending me here. I will remain here forever, away from your company. Go away at once dear brothers and be happy! You will become powerful. In return for having always tried to please you, I beg you to remember me at all your parties and ceremonies. I want you to worship me and be the first one to receive your offerings and sacrifices, since I stay in this place because of you." Manco Capac answered that they would follow his wishes and comands. Ayar Uchu promissed to give them powers and gifts to attain nobility.

Those were his last words before he was transformed into a stone.

He was made into an Inca Huaca and was named Ayar Uchu Guanacauri. It remained the most important Inca Huaca up until the Spanish arrived. It received the largest amount of offerings and it was the place used to invest Inca heroes with honours.

The remaining brothers, saddened by the deaths of Ayar Cache and Ayar Uchu, came down from the mountain and entering the Cuzco Valley arrived at a place called Matagua, they decided to remain there for a while and build huts. It was in this place where they held the "Guarachico Ceremony" (ear piercing ritual) for Sinchi Roca, son of Manco Capac and Mama Ocllo.

It is said they stayed in Matagua for two years but, they continued looking for rich and fertile land in the neighbourhood, until one day Mama Huaco who was very strong and skilful, got hold of two gold poles and threw them northwards. They flew as fast as a rifle shot, one of them landed in a place called Calcabamba but, did not sink into the soil, it was a sign of fallow land. The other reached farther up near Cuzco and sank right into the ground, it was a sign of fertile soil. The place was called Guanaypata

There is another version that says: When Manco Capac was walking past Guaynapata when he struck the gold pole, the one he always carried with him, in the soil and it sank so deep it was difficult to pull it out. This was interpreted as a sign of fertile soil. The Incas decided there and then to keep that land for themselves, even when they knew it was inhabited by other people. They went back to Matagua in order to work out a plan to conquer that area.

Manco Capac saw from Matagua a large stone in a place

called Guaynapata, right in the middle of Cuzco, in the site where Santo Domingo Monastery is today. He showed it to Ayar Auca and said: "Brother, do you remember we agreed you would go and take possession of the lands we want to conquer?. Look at the stone, fly there (Ayar Auca had developed wings), sit on the stone and guard it, because we will go and live there and populate that area."

As soon as Ayar Auca heard his brother's words, he flew to the indicated place and sat on the stone, as he did so he was transformed into a stone himself and became a sign of the possession of the Cuzco valley by the Incas. The place was called Cozco in the old language.

There were only Manco Capac and four sisters left at this point and they all decided to go and take possession of Guaynapata. When they arrived at Guaynapata (near El Arco de la Plata on the way to Charcas) they found villages inhabited by Guallas. Manco Capac and Mama Huaco besides taking away lands and water wells from the Guallas, were said to have been extremely cruel towards them.

It is said that fierce Mama Huaco after having killed a Gualla, ripped him to bits; open his rib cage; tore his lungs and heart out and ate them. Then, looking like a she devil and armed with a stone tied to a piece of rope, rushed forward to attack the other Guallas. Having witnessed the horrendous spectacle and fearing the same would happen to them, some of the Guallas ran away abandoning their land.

The Incas, having seen Mama Huaco's excesses and fearing to be seen as tyrants, could not think of anything better but to kill all the remaining Guallas in the hope that no one would hear about their crimes. They killed as many as they could expecting to erase the memory of what had happened.

Manco Capac and his people, after the dreadful deed, went down a mile southeast of Cuzco only to be attacked by Cinchi Copalimayta the warrior leader, who, in spite of being a foreigner was leading the Sauasera clan. They had seen how the Incas had taken away the Guallas lands and how cruel they had been and that is why they adopted Copalimayta to lead their army. The Sauasera won the battle and Manco Capac and his people had to go back to Guanaypata.

The Incas continued their occupation of the surrounding area and after a few months they attacked the Sauasera again, defeating them this time and even capturing Copalimayta, who escaped and abadoned the area forever. Manco Capac and Mama Huaco then seized houses and fields and along with Sinchi Roca and his wife Mama Sapaca occupied the area between two rivers as well as the Inti Cancha (Place of the Sun).

That is how the Incas founded the city of Cuzco around the Ayar Auca Stone.

Adapted from "*Historia de los Incas*" by Pedro Sarmiento de Gamboa (1530-1592)

SECOND
PART

SECOND
PART

The Turtle

Once upon a time, during a Gods' feast, there was a shortage of food. The Turtle God who since antiquity was the God of all celebrations, had been in charge of the party organization and therefore all the complains fell upon him. All the other Gods went up to the Turtle and demanded more food or at least an explanation, but the God could not offer either.

The Turtle God, in desperation, decided to sacrifice himself as a tribute to the hunger experienced by the other Gods, and allow himself to be eaten. By an act of magic the God made his meat taste like many different meats, thus each God could enjoy his or her favourite food. This is supposed to be the reason why turtle meat has different flavours and colours. Turtle meat tastes like a mix of chicken, pork and fish meat.

Nevertheless, the Gods decided to punish the Turtle God and to prevent the failure of another banquet, they exiled him from the Heavens, but gave the turtle the capacity to live without food for long periods. They also gave him sloth as an attribute, so he could never forget his lack of organization.

Besides they gave him a strong shell over his flesh so that Gods would not be tempted to have turtle meat at their banquets.

The Gods acknowledged the Turtle God's sacrifice during the banquet by allowing his meat to taste like bird' meat, fish meat and pork meat symbolizing the three elements: air, water and earth.

Extract from: Augusto D. León Barandiarán: *Mitos, leyendas y tradiciones lambayecanas*. Lima s/f.

The Painted Huaca of Illimo

A kilometer south of Illimo there is a painted Huaca and it is in this place where the old temple of the Moon, the rivers, the rain, the lizards and the spiders stood. The Temple was built in adobe and lacked any decoration.

A long time ago, before Pachacutec's reign and the conquest of Yunga territory by the Inca army, Antotunga, the temple's priest had a dream: The Sun had come down, burnt the temple to the ground and painted on the priest's face the shape of a sun to remind him who he always had to worship.

The old priest, taking no notice of the dream, continued to offer sacrifices and to worship the Moon, the Water and the Winds, until one morning when he got up and went to boil maize to prepare beer for the offerings, he found the temple completely painted in red on the outside, while the inside was painted in three colours: red for the sun; blue for the sky and yellow for gold.

The priest then felt on his face the intense heat of the Sun, as in his dream, and fell dead on the spot. He had on his face a golden mask, the sign of the Sun God.

It is said that the Sun God himself painted the Huaca of Illimo and that Antotunga's bones along with the golden mask were found at the beginning of the XX Century. This legend can also be interpreted as a sign of the Inca Conquest.

The Yucal Legend

God Wiracocha, after a long and eventful hunting excursion wondered around Yunga territory. Pressed by hunger he decided to pick up some yucas (cassava) from a yuca bush. At that time yucas were fruits that hung from branches, unlike now, where yucas are roots.

Wiracocha went into a yuca field, but when he tried to pick some of the big and tasty yucas, the yuca bushes, being selfish, made their branches fall and therefore denied the God their fruits. They had failed to recognize the God because of his clothes and his tired look. God Wiracocha in a fury, damned the yuca plant: "Because you have rebelled against your God you will never be eaten in Heaven. Men and animals will eat you, but only after they destroy you. The very fruit you produce will become your root" That is why to eat yucas now we have to destroy the whole plant.

Extract from: Francisco Izquierdo Ríos y José María Arguedas: *Canciones y cuentos del pueblo Quechua*, Editorial Huascarán, Lima 1949.

The Pachacamac Islands

A long time ago there were two Kings who hated each other. Both had children and the son of one of them fell in love with the daughter of the other one. The girls' father, once he realized what was happening locked up his daughter in his palace so she could not be seen by her lover.

The young man, in order to enter the palace, took the shape of a beautiful and colourful bird. One day, when the girl was in the garden with her female servants, the bird was caught and adopted as a pet.

A few days later the bird transformed itself back into a young man and after some months the King found out that his daughter was pregnant. The King interrogated his daughter about her pregnancy and she answered that one day she had a dream: "the bird she had in her room had become a young boy." The king realized his daughter had been fooled and ordered her execution.

She ran away in despair and when she turned back she saw a horrible bird running after her. To avoid being caught she jumped into the sea along with her son. As they fell down she became the large island and her son the small one. This is the story of the two islands opposite the Pachacamac Temple.

The Santa Elena Giants

There are some oilfields on the peninsula that the Spanish named Santa Elena. The inhabitants of the area believed two giants lived there. They were said to be as tall as four normal human beings. They did not know where the giants came from, but they knew they ate the same food as human beings. The giants also ate lots of fish, as they were good fishermen. They sailed on large boats and brought back a great variety of fish. They ate large quantities, walked around naked and were very cruel. They would kill many Indians for no reason and because of this they were greatly feared.

One day a shining young man came down from the sky and fought the giants with fire, the flames left marks on the rocks, which can still be seen. Even when the giants tried to hide in the jungle and the valleys the powerful young man was able to kill both of them.

When the Spanish arrived to Puerto Viejo (now on the Ecuador Coast) and found two figures representing the two giants, a man and a woman. They constructed a very diffe-

71

rent story: God had sent an angel to destroy the giants because they were cruel and sinful, divine justice had erased them from the face of the Earth as it had done before with Sodom and Gomorra and other places.

Extract from: cronista Agustín de Zárate: *Historia del Descubrimiento y Conquista del Perú*, edición de Jam Kermenic, Imp. Miranda, Lima 1944.

The Amarus

A long time ago, what is now the Jauja or the Mantaro Valley was covered in water. In the middle of the lake there was a large rock called Wanca. This was the resting place of the Amaru, a terrifying monster with a llama's head; two small wings; a frog's body and a long snake's tail.

One day the Rainbow God "Tulunmaya" created another Amaru as a company for the first one. The second Amaru was darker and never got to grow as much as the first one who with age had become whiter. Both monsters would fight each other over the lake and the Wanca, a resting rock which although big, was not big enough for the two Amarus to rest upon. During their fights the lake water became rough and high waves would be formed. Once when the large Amaru was attacking his rival in a fury, it even lost a large chunk of its tail.

God Ticsi, got very annoyed and sent them a storm so great, that the two Amarus were struck by lightning and died. The movement of the water and the Amarus made the lake burst and it emptied itself on the South Side.

When a valley was formed by the water that came from the lake, the first two human beings: "mama" and "taita" came out of the sacred water spring called Wari-Puquio. They had been staying inside the Earth for a long time, because they were afraid of the Amarus. The descendants of this first couple built Warivilca Temple, the ruins of which can be seen today.

The Huanca people believe the Amaru is the snake that, hidden in a cave, has grown to become a giant. The great snake, taking advantage of the winds formed during storms, tries to reach the clouds, but is destroyed by lightning. The Huancas see the shape of the Amaru in the clouds and whether the shape is black or white, is interpreted as a good or a bad omen for the year.

Cesar Toro Montalvo: *Mitos y Leyendas del Perú* , Editorial A.F.A. editores, Lima 2003.

Warivilca

After the deluge, Inti the Sun God creator of Heaven and Earth, wanted to populate the Warivilca Valley. He first sent strong winds in order to spread the water that covered the area. The Huacas (large stones) started to appear and flowers, quinua bushes, molles and alisos grew everywhere. Along the valley many water fountains appeared. It was only then that Inti , the Sun God created the first couple.

As time went by the population grew and many generations of strong men and women cultivated the land, kept herds and weaved. Eventually coming from unknown regions people arrived bringing with them blond women. They were the Yunga people.

The visitors brought "aji" (hot pepper) to trade with the Warivilca people, they explained that "aji" came from the warmer areas dominated by the Incas. The Warivilcas started relating to the Yunga women and ended up kidnapping them and locking them up in a place called Koto-Koto, where they would have sex with them.

Inti was furious about their behavior, specially because the Warivilcas and the Yungas belonged to different Ayllus (clans) and as punishment he sent the Amarus, the giant animals threw large stones amidst a deafening noise. The

Warivilcas hid in the bush and under the rocks, but it was impossible to escape from Inti's punishment. Their souls became terrible illnesses and the Yunga women were transformed into fleas.

Pitusira

There was a man called Orcco Huaranca who was arrogant and proud, he was known as a womanizer and a warrior and lived in a town called Calca.

One day after an escapade he brought along a girl he had fathered in one of his secret romances. He named the girl Pitusira. The years went by and Pitusira became a beautiful girl and was adored by Orcco Huaranca, who put one hundred women at her service and ordered five hundred soldiers to protect her.

Two commanders of the empire had fallen in love with Pitisura: Sahuasiray and Ritisiray. One day both of them went to Orcco Huaranca and asked for her hand. His answer was: "I shall give Pitisura's hand to the one who brings water to my land".

Although Ritisiray was Pitisira's favourite, both men took up the challenge. Sahuasiray built a reservoir at the top of a mountain where there was a lake, while Ritisiray brought the water through the side of a mountain called "Heart" because of its shape. The victory went to Sahuasiray who brought the water from the highlands to Orcco Huaranga's land.

Pitisura married the proud Sahuasiray, while Ritisiray attended the wedding with a broken heart and his head full of horrid thoughts. Not long after, on a stormy night, Pitisura ran away to the highlands looking for her loved one. When they met they carried on up the mountain, but the gods decided to punish them and transformed Pitisura and her lover into a monolith. That mountain remains, to this day, covered in snow and freezing cold winds.

Olga Huaita. Calca, Cuzco.

The Namla

The kings of two islands had been at war over many years. King Namla was defeated and fled along with his family and servants. They loaded as many valuables as they could upon large boats and sailed away. Having overcome many difficulties, including capsizing, they reached the coast at the mouth of the Lambayeque river.

Once on land they praised their God and performed rituals and sacrifices in his honour. They found themselves in an area with plenty of animals, along with fresh water and were pleased to find salt in abundance as well. They established themselves in that place and rapidly populated the valleys between Pacasmayo and Tumbes, including Motupe and Olmos.

When King Namla died, his people named their first settlement after his abbreviated name, they called it Nam which means water-bird. The name of King Namla's wife, Sotenic was given to the beach where they had first arrived and the name is kept until this day.

King Namla's eldest son was called Suim, he married Ciernucacum. Suim governed over many people and a large palace was built and named after him.

Modesto Rubinos y Andrade. *Priest of Morrope*. 1782.

The Alpamayo Princess

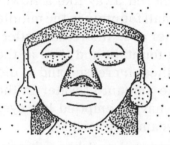

Once upon a time, under the Huandoy peak on the Andean region of Ancash, lived a hard working community, who cultivated the land and raised vicunas.

Prince Alpachayllu reigned over them. He was kind hearted and a good leader. He was also very much in love with his wife Princess Alpamayo. They lived happily over many years in their fertile and beautiful land until one ill-fated day a group of silent men arrived, they were messengers from a far away land called Conchucos. They had come to beg Prince Alpachayllu to go with them and teach them to cultivate the land and to domesticate animals, so their people could have a better life.

The good hearted Prince accepted their request and one spring morning, after having tenderly said goodbye to his wife, he departed. Princess Alpamayo was left sad and alone, counting the days for her husband's return. The palace rooms were filled with silence and her heart was filled with deep sorrow.

Meanwhile, in the land of the silent men, Prince Alpachayllu had fallen victim to the local sorceress' powers, who had made him fall in love with a young village girl. The Conchuco inhabitants had decided they could not afford to loose such an excellent leader and had asked the sorceress to use her powers to make the Prince stay with them.

When Princess Alpamayo heard of her Prince's predicament, it is said, that she withered away like a flower burned by frost. She went to a small fountain in the middle of a barren land. By looking at her own distressed reflection on the clear waters of the fountain and then at the surrounding landscape, her sadness increased and so did her tears. Her tears raised the amount of water in the fountain and after a few days, having emptied her eyes from tears, the small fountain became a large lake.

One day the Princess disappeared and her subjects, filled with sorrow and in their vain attempts to look for her, ended up going to different lands and far away towns, abandoning forever their beloved and fertile land.

Marcos Sauri. *Leyendas Ancashinas*. Huaraz.

Animal War

There was a time when all jungle animals were at war with each other. It had got to a point where hardly anyone remembered why they were fighting and no one was interested to find out either. They only remembered that the ones who started the war were the pumas and the frogs. It was said that the fight started when, on a beautiful sunny morning a puma was walking to the river to get a drink of water. While a frog was sun bathing in the grass on the river bank and on its way, the puma accidently stepped on the frog's head.

Hey! Said the frog: Can't you see where you put your dirty paw?

The puma turned around and hit the frog knocking him into the water.

The frog was furous and spat at the puma. At this point, both went away and began gathering supporters. Two armies were formed, the frogs on one side and the pumas on the other.

The frogs recruited: Ants, scorpions and piranhas, while the pumas recruited the dreaded flying snakes, who at once came out to hunt their new enemies.

The frogs then asked the horseflies for their support, they swore to attack the pumas day and night. The frogs also recruited the help of the spiders, who silently and laboriously began knitting their deathly webs. The bees were also recruited and attacked in small swarms, making the puma's lives miserable.

The pumas, on the other hand, asked for the help of the *sajinos*, the *anases*, the wolves and even the crocodiles, who ecstatic at the idea of war, went in and out of the river, shaking their tails and splashing so much that the amount of water in the rivers diminished.

Over time, it was clear that the frogs were supported by small animals. Insignificant in size and almost invisible, they gathered on the low lands, lakes and river shores. While the pumas had recruited large, powerful and awesome animals, who dominated the highlands and mountain peaks.

Hostilities went on for a long time, until one happy day, an old turtle had a moment of lucidity and suggested: Let's choose one animal from each side to fight each other and the winner will claim victory for his entire side.

The large animals listened and clapped at the proposal, while the small animals took their time to discuss it but, eventually accepted it too.

Immediately a few meetings took place amongst the large animals. Each of them argued to be the strongest and the bravest and therefore the one with the qualities to be chosen to defeat the enemy.

The crocodile speaking with a harsh voice said: I am the right contestant.

A monkey hanging from a tree dared to say: You should, to start with, stop moving your tail because it is bothering me.

What? Asked the crocodile frowning.

To tell you the truth, claimed the monkey, you don't frighten anyone, you are far too heavy to fight.

On hearing this, the beast blind with fury hit the tree with its tail causing the unwary monkey balancing on a thin branch to fall down and many birds, who were on the branches, flew away to safety.

There and then, a frightening snake with its back bearing the marks of a butterfly, slither in and fixing her gleaming eyes on the crowd of animals, said with her whistling voice: Who can resist the power of my sight? Who can stand my poison that brings death?. These words made the teeth of the many deer present chatter with fright and they all ran away across the fields.

The majestic tiger got up and roared: Stop it!. While filing its nails on a stone and without looking at anyone said: Stop at once this ridiculous argument. Who around here dares to doubt the superiority of the mighty tiger?. Who?. It took an awesome jump and walked around staring at each one of the animals present. For a moment no one dared to mutter a sound, not even to breathe, let alone disagree with such a powerful character. Thus the tiger was elected to represent his side at the fight. At the end of the gathering the tiger smiled arrogantly. Enjoying his triumph, it remained at the meeting place, patiently twisting its whiskers.

The frogs camp was silent, one could see the small animals run from one side to the other, bent up as if carrying some heavy load. It was difficult to know who had been elected to fight the tiger. A darkness, like a jungle night, covered the name of the contestant. It was a secret.

The large animals did not even bother to find out the name of the enemy. Meanwhile, animals from both sides prepared the field for the fight, picking up leaves and measuring borders. The large animals organized a party to celebrate the tiger's victory and they even hired musicians to play all night until dawn.

The chosen day had arrived and from very early in the morning the surrounding area to the designated field, began to fill with animals who took positions on the trees, shrubs and hills. Very soon the area was covered with herons, monkeys, ducks, otorongos (small Amazonian tigers) and snakes. Fish and alligators looked upon from a small lake.

The large animals were excited and the small ones were nervous. It was a special occasion because it meant the end of the war. Everyone was happy, as they had not been for a long time, they shook hands and greeted each other kindly.

The time for the fight arrived and not wasting a second, the tiger jumped from a tree branch on to the field. The tiger looked splendid and the animals on its side greeted it with claps and shouts of joy.

Everyone looked around expecting to see the tiger's rival, but there was no sight of anyone anywhere.

The tiger roared boastfully. Is the enemy so scared of me that they refuse to send a contestant?. It laughed.

At that precise moment, the tiger felt a painful sting in the most sensitive part of its groin. It bent forward, as fast as lightening and scratched its skin with its claws. Then the tiger felt the sting on its haunch, then it turned around and tore at its skin.

The contestant was the tiny "isango", armed with a sharp sting. The small animal ran from the tiger's stomach to its back, piercing its skin everywhere, causing the wounds to swell and burst like volcanoes.

In a few minutes the tiger was drowning in its own blood. The audience was astounded. It looked as if the tiger had lost its mind under the influence of a drug prepared by the frogs. The frogs then raised their heads and shouted the name of their contestant and the word Isango went around through all the villages.

Meanwhile the tiger ran around as if on flames and jumped up and down clawing at the air. Its roars managed to bend far away trees. Turning its claws and teeth against itself the tiger foamed at the mouth and tore its skin.

Finally the isango stung the enemy in the eye and it gave such loud scream that many cockatoos fell down from the high guava trees. The tiger saw the sun roll down until it got tangled up in the wounded animal's own eyelashes. The tiger heard the flapping of the herons' wings as they left and felt the sweet taste of blood in its mouth, the taste brought it back to the time when it lay by its mother. The tiger held tight to that memory.

The animals from both sides saw how the tiger fell heavily on the ground, with its legs bent upwards. This is how the small animals wan the war and claimed for themselves the sun, the earth, the water and the stars.

Danilo Sanchez Lihon. *Mil y Una Hogueras*. INLIL. 1991.

Death of Three Pishtacos

 **There was a** miner called Joaquin Ingaroca who was born in Comas. He had worked for five years in the Tacarpanja mine and was returning to his village after a long absence. He was travelling on foot, as there was no other form of transport at the time. He left at six in the morning and walked lost in thought, but fearing being mugged by pishtacos or huaicacos during his solitary journey. He was scared of loosing his small savings, gathered over the long years he worked at the mine.

Towards midday he reached a village where he bought some coca leaves and a litre of "canazo"(which is a type of rum) for his journey. He knew the way to Comas and the fact that there were no other villages on the way, only uninhabited lands watched over by pishtacos. Thus he continued his journey, chewing his coca leaves and occasionally, taking a drink. To pluck up courage, he sang some of the songs that were traditional during pay day parties at the mine. Up until then, the coca leaves tasted sweet in his mouth and he enjoyed the taste of the canazo, this was interpreted as a good omen and he felt that nothing bad would happen to him.

Joaquin kept walking when night arrived and the moon came out on the high planes of the Andes known as "La Puna". He lit a cigarette to steady his nerves, but suddenly it went out. He tried to light it again, but the cigarette split in the middle. On top of that the coca leaves in his mouth turned bitter. He had a drink, but it did not make him feel better. Joaquin took all these as signs that a disgrace was about to occur and he fell prey to fear. He looked at the stars and realized that it was about nine and he felt tired and breathless, so he looked for a cave where to rest. Thanks to the bright moon he was able to find one and once inside, he took another handful of coca leaves to chew.

The miner had rested for a while when he heard the bellow of a bull who seemed to be near by. He thought that perhaps the bull slept where he was, so he climbed up on to some protruding rocks on the upper part of the cave and huddled up in a hole filled with "ichu" (highland grass). The bull, in fact, entered the cave and looked around and sniffed everywhere, aware that there was someone inside. The bull tried to jump to the upper part of the cave, but luckily the protruding rocks stopped it.

Poor old Joaquin watched the bull trying to get him and trembling with fear prayed and begged God to protect him. The bull after having failed time and again to reach Joaquin's hiding place, felt tired and lay on the cave's floor and fell asleep. While the bull snored, Joaquin stayed up thinking and chewing his coca leaves. After a while he heard a horse galloping on the stony ground outside the cave. It was a pishtaco who had seen Joaquin going into the cave, thus after having tied his horse he went in convinced he would find his victim. The pishtaco pulled his knife out and placed it on the sleeping bull. Unfortunately the knife hit the bull's horn, waking the bull up. The bull stood up and attacked the pishtaco who fell on the floor, where the bull trod on him and ripped his stomach open, only stopping when the body was torn apart

Having finished with the pishtaco, the bull left the cave bellowing and went to his usual pastures, it was around midnight

The miner then came down from the top of the cave and found the pishtaco in a sorry state under his torn poncho. He found and picked up the long and sharp knife and tried to mount the pishtaco's horse, but the horse refused to be mounted. At every new attempt to get near it, the horse kicked and threatened the miner with his hoofs. Joaquin then thought that perhaps if he put on the pishtaco's torn poncho the horse would let him mount it and the trick worked.

Happy to be riding a horse, Joaquin tried to go towards his village, but the horse refused to go in that direction. On the contrary, it started galloping to the opposite direction in spite of Joaquin's attempts to stop it. The horse was going at great speed to the pishtaco's house. They galloped through valleys, rivers and mountains until they arrived at a large cave.

At this point the miner dismounted, filled with apprehension at what would happen. He went cautiously inside the cave and found a woman sitting on the floor, he realized she did not have feet, her legs ended at the knees. Surprised to see a stranger come in the cave, she asked Joaquin who he was. He told her all about the cave and the pishtaco's death.

The woman said: There were three pishtacos, the other two are about to arrive, if you have the courage to kill both of them stay and I shall help you, but if you don't have it, leave at once.

Joaquin assured her that he could kill the two pishtacos if she told him how to do it.

The woman with no feet answered: When they come in, they eat and then come near me, put their heads on my knees and ask me to scratch their heads to sleep, while I do so they fall asleep. It is then when you should come out and behead them with your knife.

Joaquin accepted the woman's plan and both started to plot. The woman showed him the cave and advised him to hide. The miner then went into the confines of the cave. First he found an opening which led to a large room where there were many bodies hanging and dripping fat, drop by drop. Next, he found a large number of ribs of different colours; sacks of flour and sugar and many boxes full of money. There were also an assortment of objects which must have been the possessions of the pishtacos' victims.

After a while, as he was hiding amongst the various objects, the pishtacos arrived on horse. The woman served them their meals then, as predicted, they lay by her and resting their heads on her knees fell into heavy sleep. When they started to snore, the woman made a sign to Joaquin to carry out their plan. The miner came out holding the knife, got next to the pishtacos, beheading one of them and then the other. The woman helped him to tear the heads away from the bodies.

He then helped the woman on to one of the horses,

placed the boxes with money on the other and finally left, riding towards his village. When he got there he bought houses and fields and lived as a rich man from then on.

Pedro. S. Monge. *Cuentos Orales del Rio Mantaro*. Literaturas Andinas. 1988.

The Pongo's Dream

A man was walking towards the Hacienda Owner's house, he was going to perform his duty as a servant. He was a Pongo and as such, his duty was to take turns with other Pongos, serving for free at the Hacienda Owner's house.

He was small built, dressed in rags and had a weak character. In all, he looked miserable.

When the Pongo greeted the Hacienda Owner in the house corridor, the latter could not stop laughing and asked him, in front of the male and female servants: What are you a human being or a thing?.

The humble Pongo did not answer, scared and with frozen eyes he stood by.

The Hacienda Owner carried on: Come on! He must at least know how to wash pots or hold a broom with those useless hands. Take away this piece of trash! He yelled at the man in charge of the servants.

The Pongo went on his knees and kissed the Hacienda Owner's hands and with his head down he followed his new boss to the kitchen. Although the Pongo was small built he was as strong as any other man. Whatever he was ordered to do he would do well, but he looked spooked out. Some of the other servants laughed and others felt sorry for him. The mestizo cook said when she saw him: " Orphan

93

amongst orphans, the coldness in his eyes must come from the cold moon wind and his heart is full of sorrow."

The Pongo did not talk to anyone, he worked quietly and ate in silence. He obeyed everyone's orders and one could only hear him say: "Yes, my Lord, Yes, my Lady."

The Hacienda Owner took a special dislike to the Pongo, the reason was not clear. Perhaps it was because of his spooked out look; perhaps because of the rags he wore or perhaps even because of his refusal to talk. Anyway, at dusk, when all the servants got together to pray the Hail Mary in the corridor of the hacienda house, the Pongo would be tortured in front of everyone. The Hacienda Owner would shake him as if he were a rag. He would push the Pongo's head down and force him to kneel, while on his knees the Hacienda Owner would pat him on the face and say: "I believe you are a dog. Bark!".

The poor man could not bark.

The Hacienda Owner ordered: "Go on all fours."

The Pongo would obey and walk a few steps on all fours.

The Hacienda Owner would carry on ordering: "Trot sideways, like a dog."

The Pongo knew how to run imitating the small highland dogs. The Hacienda Owner was pleased and laughed, his whole body would shake with his laughter.

When the trotting servant woud reach the other side of the long corridor, the Hacienda Owner shouted: "Come back!"

Trotting sideways the Pongo would return, he arrived breathless.

Meanwhile some of his fellow servants would pray the Hail Mary. They quietly prayed.

The Hacienda Owner would order the tired Pongo:

"Prick your ears vizcacha (Type of Andean rodent)". "You are a vizcacha". "Sit on your hind legs and clap your hands."

As if inside his mother's womb he had been influenced by a vizcacha, the Pongo could mimic those animals when they stay still on the rocks, as if they were praying, although obviously he could not prick his ears. It was then when some of the hacienda servants would burst into laughter.

Kicking him softly with his boot the Hacienda Owner would knock the Pongo down, onto the corridor's brick floor.

"Let's pray the Our Father." The Hacienda Owner would say to his Indians, who were waiting in a queue.

The Pongo would get up slowly, but he could not pray because he was not in his designated place.

Well into the night the servants would go down the corridor to the patio and then towards the servants' head-quarters.

"Go away Pancita!." The Hacienda Owner would some-times order the Pongo.

Everyday the Hacienda Owner would make the Pongo roll around in front of the other servants. He would force the Pongo to laugh or to pretend he was crying. He would expose him to be mocked by his fellow servants and tenant farmers. Until one day, at the time when they prayed the Hail Mary and the corridor was crowded with all the hacienda workers. When the Hacienda Owner started to look at the Pongo with his deep-set eyes, the Pongo spoke clearly although his face looked slightly horrified.

"Great Lord, give me license, my dear Lord, I want to talk to you."

The Hacienda Owner did not listen to what he had heard and asked: "What?. Have you spoken or has someone else?.."

"Your permission to talk to you dear Lord. It is you who I want to talk to." Replied the Pongo.

"Speak if you may." Answered the Hacienda Owner.

"My Lord, my Master, my Dearest." The Pongo started to talk. "Last night I dreamed that we died together, together we died."

"With me? You? Tell me everything." Said the Hacienda Owner.

"As we were dead men, my Lord, we appeared naked, both, together. Naked before our Great Father St. Francis.

"And then? Speak!" Ordered the Hacienda Owner, he was annoyed and restless with curiosity.

"Our Great Lord St. Francis seeing us dead, naked and together, examined us with his eyes that reach and measure God knows what distances. He examined you and I thinking, I believe, in each of our hearts and what we were and what we are. Like the rich and great man that you are, my Lord, you confronted those eyes."

"What about you?"

"I can not know how I was , Great Lord, I am unable to know what am I worth."

"O'right. Carry on speaking."

"Our Father then spoke and the words that came out of his own mouth were: Let the most beautiful angel come, he should be accompanied by a small angel , who should be as beautiful as the former. The small angel should bring a golden goblet which must be filled with the most transparent sugar cane honey."

"What happened next?" asked the Hacienda Owner.

The Indian servants listened to the Pongo with great attention, but in fear.

"My Master, continued the Pongo, the moment our Father St Francis gave the order, a shining angel appeared, it was as high as the Sun. Walking slowly, it moved until it was in front of our Father. Behind that angel walked a smaller one, beautiful and glowing with the soft light of a flower. It was carrying a golden goblet."

"What happened next?" Repeated the Hacienda Owner.

"Our Great Lord ordered: Angel, cover this gentleman with the honey in the golden goblet, your hands should be as soft as feathers when they touch the man's body. That is how the sublime angel, holding the honey in his hands covered your whole body, from head to toe. You straightened up alone and your shining body stood out against the sky, glowing as if you were made of gold, almost transparent."

"That is how it should be." Said the Hacienda Owner and then asked: "And what about you?"

"While you were shining in the sky, our Lord St Francis ordered again: All the angels from Heaven should come and the most ordinary and worthless ones should bring a can filled with human excrement."

"And then?"

"A lower rank angel with flaky legs and with hardly enough strength to keep its wings in their place arrived in front of our Lord. It arrived very tired and with droopy wings, carrying a large can in its hands."

"Our Great Lord ordered the angel: Listen, old thing. Cover the body of this poor man with the excrement inside the can you have brought. Cover his whole body anyway you can. At once!"

"Then the old angel with its bony hands, scooped the excrement out of the can and unevenly covered my body, carelessly, as one throws mud over the wall of an ordinary house. In the sky glow the angel seemed embarrassed, stinking."

"That is how it should be." Agreed the Hacienda Owner. "Carry on! Or is that how it ends?"

"No my Lord, my Master. When we were both together again in front of our Lord St Francis, even when we were together in a different way. He looked at us again, He looked at you and He looked at me, for a long time. I can not possibly know the depth his eyes, which filled the sky, reached. He mixed night and day, oblivion and memory. Then he said: Everything the angels had to do with you has been done. Now, lick each other! Slowly, for a long time. At that moment the old angel became young and its wings recovered their black colour and great strength. Our Lord entrusted that angel with making sure his will would be carried out.

Adapted from: J.M. Arguedas. 1969.

The Fox and the Huaychao

 **A long time** ago a fox had a small mouth and it was not a gossip. One day, while going for a walk it saw a huaychao singing on a hill. The huaychao was as small as a thrush, it had light gray feathers and while it sang it moved its white feathered tail. The fox stared at the bird's long, flute like beak and said cunningly: "What a beautiful flute my friend and you play it so well. Would you lend it to me, just for one moment?. I will play it carefully."

The bird refused, but the cajoling fox insisted so much, that the huaychao eventually lent it its beak, advicing the fox to sew its mouth before playing so the flute could fit better. Thus the fox played the flute around the hill, after a while the huanchao asked for its beak back, but the fox refused.

The bird said then: "I only play it every now and then and you play it all the time."

The fox carried on playing the flute regardless of the huaychao's pleads. It played on and on to a group of small animals who had gathered around.

The noise woke some anases (skunks) up. They came out of their caves and merrily went up the hill. When they got near the fox they began to dance and were followed by all the other animals. It was hard for the fox to keep a straight face, suddenly it burst into laughter and its stitched up mouth ripped open. Its mouth was so big that it almost reached its ears.

The beak fell down and before the fox could regain its composure, the huaychao picked it up and flew away.

It is said that ever since and as punishment for their betrayal of trust, foxes have large mouths.

The Mother of all Stones

One day Don Esteban Herrera left his farm to go to the Colca river to fetch his cattle, as the cold season had arrived. All of a sudden he heard the chihuanco (type of bird) singing, which forecasts strong rain. Don Esteban smiled. Amidst the molle (sacred tree) branches the chihuanco exposed its spotty backside to the rain, so the water would stop it stinging.

Going passed Don Genaro Luque's farm, he heard children playing and singing: "Rain rain, come again. The old lady is in her cave." A thought crossed his mind: Had the chihuanco tried to warn him of something?, but he got distracted thinking ho had to greet Don Genaro Luque.

As Don Esteban Herrera walked on he remembered being woken up by a couple of tankas (birds) who let him know it would be fine to sow by the river bank that year and not to fear February's rains. Thus when the Agriculture Ministry engineers arrived and said: "How can you do this? Don't you know that your fields will be flooded?."

Full of confidence he answered: "The birds have come to tell me that there will not be floods this year." To prove his point he even took the engineers to the place where the tancas had made their nests. "Didn't I tell you?. If there were to be floods, birds would not stay by the river banks."

The engineers said: "The river will take everything away, we want to see you when that happens."

It never happened, Don Esteban's maize grew very well by the river bank, being watered by the Colca river itself and the tancas had many chicks. He would have liked to see the engineers' faces for a laugh, but they never came back.

The children were still singing: "Rain rain come again. The old lady is in her cave." As Don Esteban Herrera went in to greet Don Genaro he could hear the noise made by the guinea pigs: "cui, cui, cui..."

He told Don Genaro: " I am going to collect my animals. I left them grazing at Oroyapata hill."

"You better hurry Don Esteban before the rain comes and if you see Erasmo, please tell him that I need him."

Don Esteban finished his glass of beer and left in a hurry saying good bye to Don Genaro.

On the Maripampa plain, the wind and the purple clouds, that looked like dirty cotton wool, made him feel uneasy. "Will it be a bad omen?." He remembered the chihuancos calling for rain, but as he was in a hurry he put that thought away. He then licked his index finger and lifted his hand to find out where the wind would bring the rain from. His finger got numb with cold and turned green, alfalfa green in fact.

Didn't he realized it was another warning?. Was he that scatty?. Suddenly loud thunder was heard coming from behind the mountains he could not see. Don Esteban counted up to forty two between thunder and came to the conclusion that the storm was forty two kilometers away.

"Strong!. It will be very strong." He said to himself. He went into the thick fog faster and more nervous as usual and he suddenly heard a very loud noise. The stone we all know as Corokanca, started to move. "It can not be true." He thought, trying not to listen to such a loud noise.

The Corokanca walked, darkening the plain. The loud

noise, louder than thunder was making him deaf. The storm was only about fifteen kilometers away.

What would happen to him in a place where no one could imagine him, let alone see him? To help himself out of his confusion he reasoned: "This is Mother Nature after all." Then he remembered the great stone was seventy meters long. As a way of consolation he thought: "It is the Corokanca after all, if it were an animal it could be a worm as fat as a mountain.". The powerful stone, as white as chalk on its upper side blocked his path .

"Corokanca, I am on my way to collect my animals, they are on Oroyapata hill. Let me through Corokanca!."

As if it was answering him, the mother of all stones made a slight movement. He trembled with fear, wondering what would happen to him? or was he looking at the last images his eyes would ever see?. What about his wife, his children, his fields?. He saw himself dying a dreadful death, far away, left to his own devices, very far to where he belonged and far also of the things that kept him alive. Would the long and wide Maripampa plain be his unknown grave?.

Just as the Corokanca was about to reach the Colca river, Don Esteban, having reached the end of his tether, panic stricken, shouted with all his might: "The devil is moving the stone!. The devil itself!."

The stone, caressed by the last drops of that February rain as it was very close to the river, suddenly stopped. Why did it stop?. Wasn't it all going well?.

The stone got frightened by poor Don Esteban's screams. Not only that, but when it was about to jump and lie like a stone bridge over the river, the sudden stop almost broke it in half and left its borders cracked.

At that very moment the inhabitants of Tisco and Cota-

Cota villages felt terribly sad. Those two villages needed the bridge more than any others. They needed it to transport their fruits and vegetables, specially when the river level grew and flooded its banks.

They were very sorry that the broken Corokanca had stopped just at the side of the Colca river. On top of that, stupid Don Esteban kept screaming and shouting and naming the devil.

They all knew that not even the torrential February rains would have made the river current strong enough to move the bridge, made by the beautiful and strong mother of all stones.

That afternoon of blue hail stones, the whole of the Caylloma area, bathed by the Colca river, fell prey to sadness.

"It is all my fault" regreted Don Esteban "if only I had understood the messages of the chihuancos, or the fact that my finger went green. What can I do now?

The villagers continued to look at the Colca valley and its river, at its ravines full of kenua, the material used to thatch their roofs and at the trola, the fire wood for their stoves. They looked at the other side of the river, at the Topay district and even farther away, at Conocota. They looked at their neighbours who can not have their labour; who did not share their feasts nor their yaravies (sad Andean songs). They also looked at the woods and other villages that needed their strenght and joy, as much as they needed theirs, but they were still isolated.

It is said that Don Esteban died of sadness, thinking that because of his fear and screams, the villagers were left without a much needed bridge. Wouldn't it have been easier to remain quiet and to look respectfully at the work of the mother of all stones?.

Some say that his family abandoned him, others that he left his family. The truth is that the chihuancos and the tankas took Don Esteban to a far away place and at night we can hear his pain, when he plays his flute and the wind makes the alfalfa fields shine.

Cesar Vega Herrera. Colca, Arequipa (Unpublished).

The Yacu-Mama

The main entertainment for some Iquitos'
inhabitants was to go to the quay to look at the Brazilian
steam ships arrive and at the same time to look at the
choppy water under the pier (the Muyuna).

It was said that the day Remigio died the Yaku-Mama
was furious...

Remigio and Donatilda had been married for just a
week. Dona Regina, Donatilda's mother had moved in with
the young and hard working couple. By being affectionate
and friendly towards Remigio she tried to dispel her image
of the wicked mother in law.

Remigio had been working at the wharf for a long time.
The Yaku-Mama lived under the pier and the iron pilars, at
the bottom of the river and was protected by the Muyuna.
The Yaku-Mama was said to be a two headed monster with
a snake like body that measured between twenty and thirty
meters from head to tail.

The Yaku-Mama was the mother of all rivers, including
the Amazon. It taught the water how to flow and meander.
When there was a shipwreck or a small boat capsized or
when people drowned, including the most expert of
swimmers, it was believed that the Muyana wanted to
provide food for its mother's insatiable belly.

Some of the wharf workers said that at nights they could
hear the rattling rings of the monster just before it took
new victims, which it did after its long digestive periods.
They were convinced they could even see two powerful

lights at the bottom of the river coming from the Yaku-Mama's eyes.

Dona Regina knew more about the monster than most, because over her long life she had heard many stories about the Yaku-Mama. That day when she heard her son in law mention that the Yaku-Mama was furious she said: "It probably can not find food, she only eats drowned people. Since you work at the docks, be very careful my son."

That afternoon there was a lot of cargo to desembark and the work had to be done fast. It must have been four in the afternoon when one of the cages full of cargo, that was being lowered down by a crane, hit Remigio and he fell down a whole meter before he reached the water. His fellow workers who saw the accident said that Remigio, who had been supervising the operation, had fallen right in the middle of the Muyana, which swallowed him to give him to the monster's open jaws, thus satisfying its hunger.

Hours later, Donatilda, surrounded by friends and family, cried her eyes out. While Dona Regina, looking older than ever and with eyes filled with tears, which never run down her thin cheeks, kept repeating: "It was meant to be. I told him so!."

Juan Diaz del Aguila. *Folklore Amazónico.*

The Turtle and the Fox

 **One day the** turtle was going to visit her relatives and on her way it met a fox.

The fox asked the turtle "Is it true you can put up with hunger for a very long time?"

The turtle aswered that it could live without food for two months. The fox said it could be without food for three months. It was then they decided to have a contest.

To start with the fox told the turtle to go into a hole and not come out until the tamamuri fruit had riped. The fox said it would let the turtle know when it happened.

The turtle agreed and went into the hole. It stayed there for weeks without dying of hunger. The tamamuri fruit ripen, but the fox did not tell the turtle. It only asked the turtle to come out after the tamaruri season had been and gone.

The turtle came out of the hole at the fox's request and did not say anything.

It was the fox's turn to go into the hole.

The turtle told the fox it should stay in until the hen's eggs burst open and the chicks started to grow. The turtle said it would let the fox know when it happen.

Three days went by and the turtle went to see the fox and called: "Fox my friend, fox come out" but the fox did not answer.

The turtle then went inside the hole, looked around and was surprised to see that the fox was already dead. The fox hadn't even lasted a week.

The turtle won the contest because it ate soil while the fox died because it was stupid.

"El Origen de la Cultura Shipibo" VV.AA. Ucayali 1998.

The Heavens, the Earth and the Hedgehog

In the beginning, the heavenly dome was not as high as it is now. The space that divided Heaven and Earth was only the hight of a large tree. The Machiguengas (an Amazonian tribe), the Viracochas (Europeans) and the Punarunas (Andean people) were, at the time, very generous.

One could hear from Earth the laughter of the Saangarite (the good spirits who lived in Heaven).

Heaven had a type of umbilical cord which linked it to Earth., it was called "omoguito inkite". In fact, the Earth was suspended by that umbilical cord. The appendage was also a ladder and the Machiguengas could climb into Heaven (inkite) and go in through a hole situated at the root of the cord. The Saangarites used it also to come down to Earth (kipachi) for visits.

Viracochas, Machiguengas and Punarunas spoke the same language: Machiguenga and they all lived in harmony. There was only one bad person amongst them and everytime he went up to Heaven and the Saanganites invited him to drink masato (beer made out of manioc root or cassava) he drunk until he fell down, while the others would only drink enough to be merry. The Saanganite did not want to be visited by this man, so they decided to cut the cord and allow the Earth to fall down into the abyss. As soon as the good men heard about this plan they gathered their arms, clothes, pots and the rest of their belongings and climbed up to Heaven in order to be safe.

The man who drunk too much eventually heard about everyone climbing up to safety, so he also gathered his stuff in a bundle and hurried to climb up still holding his arrows in one hand.

When the boozer started to climb up the ladder was empty. Some of the good men were already safe in Heaven, but some were still on Earth. He thought he was safe as he was about to get into Heaven, but at that moment the Saanganite cut the appendage. Heaven went up where we see it now, while the Earth plummeted down disappearing into the abyss, except for that bit of Earth where some of the good people were, and so they were safe. When the boozer fell down, the arrows he had in his hand went into his back and he became a hedgehog.

The bit of Earth where the Machiguengas were, remained suspended for a few minutes and it was there where the hedgehog fell. The new Earth appeared and the Machiguengas and the hedgehog jumped on it. Once they all jumped the bit of old Earth fell down too.

When the Machiguengas, the Viracochas and the Punarunas lived in the old Earth they were free from illnesses and death, but in the new Earth, the one that exists now, there is illness and death and even the Machiguengas acquired bad habits.

Fray Enrique Alvarez. *"Misiones Dominicanas del Peru"* Numero 116. 1940.

The Trip to Heaven

A long time ago, the Moon was a man named Nantu who had a wife called Awju. Neither of them like to eat cassava, their favourite food was pumpkin. Nantu would send his wife to the fields collecting pumpkins while he would go hunting in the mountains.

Nantu returned and waited for a long time until his wife arrived at the house, bringing some very green pumpkins. This occurred many times, thus he decided to spy on his wife. In fact he saw her gathering ripe pumpkins, she opened a pumpkin and ate until she had enough. She would then return home with some green pumpkins and would keep her mouth close so her husband would not find out how greedy she had been.

One day, Nantu the Moon decided to go away to Heaven. He carefully made a rope and chose a dark night for his journey. Having left his wife sleep he started to climb and did not stop until he reached the place where we see the Moon today.

Awju, the wife, woke up and realizing her husband's absence she started to climb calling his name.

When Awju was about to catch up with Nantu he cut the rope and his wife fell down and crashed on to the black and fertile soil. As she crashed, her stomach split open and all the pumpkin she had ever eaten came out and mixing with the soil, became the pumpkin colour clay that the Aguarunas (Amazonian tribe) use to make their pottery.

The rest of her body became an Awju, the bird that sings in the bush during New Moon. It can only be heard during those three nights, you never hear it at any other time. It is a small bird with a wide but short beak.

Efrain Morote Best. "*Aldeas Sumergidas*" Cuzco 1988.

APENDIX

Peruvian Flora and Fauna

The following contains scientific and Quechua names of animals and plants, as well as their description by Carmelon Berrocal Evanan, a peruvian farmer from Ayacucho in the Central Andes.

MAMMALS

GUINEA PIG. *Cavia Porcellus*. Cuy or Kuwi in Quechua. It is a rodent which looks like a rat without a tail. It feeds its offspring with milk; eats vegetables and its meat is considerd a delicacy in the Andean region.
Shamans use black guinea pigs in their rituals to cure the sick.

WEASEL. *Mustela Frenata*. Unchuchuco in Quechua. It is carnivorous; measures about twenty five centimeters and it is light brown. My fellow farmers hunt them and use their skin as a sack to keep silver coins. It is believed that if you ever fill the sack up you loose it.

WILD CAT. *Lynchailurus Pajeros*. Usqu in Quechua. It is a wild animal which looks like a cat; lives in the countryside and feeds on birds. It is striped gray and likes to steal our hens at night.

SEA LION. *Otaria Flavescens*. Sometimes we call it hairless wolf or mongrel wolf. We recognize them by the marks on their bodies. Their pointed ears point backwards. When they open their mouths to eat fish their mouths make a circle.

VICUNA. *Lama Vicugna*. Wicuna in Quechua. They live in the highland plains of the Andes. They are light brown and we believe they belong to God Urqu.

MONKEY. *Alovatta Palliata*. Kusillo in Quechua. Its head is shaped like a pyramid. We have observed that the females carry their offspring on their backs.

BAT. *Phyllostomus sp*. or Desmodus rotundos. Masu in Quechua. It is a flying night mammal. It flyes and lives in ravines and caves in warm areas. Bats have black and hairless wings and they are believed to have nails on their wings. Their ears look like fox's ears and their teeth look like those of a mouse. Bats, after having slept all day, come out at night looking for food. They bite bits of flesh out of other animals and make them cry. They also bite pigs and horses' ears.

PUMA. *Puma Concolor*. Machu in Quechua. It is a very agile feline. It is an expert hunter of domestic animals, specially small pigs, hens, calfs and young donkeys. When pumas come to our farms and kill some of our animals, all the neighbouring farmers have a meeting to decide whether to hunt them down or just chase them away.

DOG. *Canis Familiaris*. Alqo in Quechua. It is a very popular pet. Dogs follow men everywhere. The hairless dog was a pet in Peru during the Inca period. All other dogs are said to have been brought by the Spanish conquerors.

DEER. *Hipocamelus Antisensis*. Taruka in It is a wild animal which lives in the mountains. My grandfather has seen many deer on the mountains wearing orange and yellow earrings, he told me they belong to the Apus, the mountain Gods.

FOX. *Pseudalopex Culpeaus*. Atuq in Quechua. When foxes kill or wound our sheep and goats the herdsmen build traps to catch them. We believe that fox's tails bring luck and wealth, that is the reason why we all keep one at home.

BIRDS

OWL. *Otus sp*. Tuko in Quechua. It is a night bird, the size of an average hen. Owls live in ravines and sleep during the day, the same as bats. They come out at night to feed, mainly mice and birds. We believe owls forecast death. Their cry sounds like: "It will end. It will end. Your life will soon end".

CONDOR. *Vultu Gryphus*. Condor in Quechua. It is the biggest Andean bird. The males have white feathers around their necks, which look like white scarfs. My grandparents told me many stories about these animals.

LARK. *Pheucticus*. Tuya in Quechua. It lives in warm areas. It is the same size as a parrot and produces a beautiful sound. It is yellow with black feather spots. Larks eat prickly pears as well as maize from our fields. They teach their chicks to sing from a very early age.

WILD DOVE. *Zenaida Asiatica*. Kukuli in Quechua. It is gray and it is the only bird that stores food for times of scarcity. It is said that people who find a dove's storage place have a lucky soul.

PARTRIDGE. *Nothoprocta*. Yutu in Quechua. It inhabits the Highland plains and it is just about as large as a hen. It feeds on insects and grass. It is believed that the partridge song forecasts rain.

YANAVICU. *Plegadis Ridgwayi*. Yanaviku in Quechua. It appears in the the Highland plains during the rainy season, but where does this migrant bird come from, I don't know.
It is a black bird with a long beak and large claws, but it has a small body.

FLORA

CUSTARD APPLE. *Annona Cherimolia*. Chirimoya in Spanish. It is a fruit of the size of an apple. Its pulp is soft, white and sweet. We use it to make ice cream, cakes and wine.
It is said to help digestion. We marinate the seeds and use the liquid against louse infestation..

ICHU. *Stipa Ichu*. Ichu in Quechua. It is a grass indigenous to the cold Andean Highlands. Many animals like: llamas, vicunas, horses, sheep, a rodent called "vizcacha", etc. feed on it. We also use it as building material in our houses: Mixed with mud for the walls and to thatch our roofs.
We beg permission from the Apus, the mountain Gods, before we pull it out because we believe ichu is the mountains' moustache. We use this grass ashes as a natural dye

MAGUEY. *Agave Americano*. It has large leaves of a blue gray colour. It is a very useful plant. We drink its sweet juice for breakfast and we make jam with its pulp. When we are young we use its leaves as blackboards to practice writing on.

MOLLE. *Haplorhus Peruviana* or *schinus molle*. Molle in Quechua. It is a large tree with a broad crown with plenty of branches with hunging leaves. We draw its resin and use it to oil our violin strings as we believe it improves their sound. We use its wood to make clogs, which we wear to dance at Christmas parties.

Molle's fruit are branches of pink berries, which we use to brew beer "upi" in Quechua and its leaves to cure people with "wind sickness", as well as, to obtain the light green dye we use to paint. The powderized seedss are used as a spicy condiment

There are male and female molles. The male molle does not yeild fruit, but the female molle, being female, does.

BROOM. *Spartium Junceum*. Retama in Spanish. This plant grows on river banks and flowers most of the year. It is said the broom flower infusion cures headaches.

SANKAY *Echinopsis Pachonoi*. It is also called Kaktu. It is a suculent plant that grows on hot areas. It flowers in November and December and its fruits, which are delicious, are ready to be picked around March and April.

CHILI. Capsicum Pubescens. Uchu in Quechua. We grow it in our gardens. It yields its fruit all through the year. There are yellow and red chilies. We use it as a green and for its hot flavour. It is also used against tooth ache, bee, wasp and spider sting and to alliviate rheumatism, tonsolitis and to cure hiccups.

MARROW. Cuncurbita Ficifolia. Wingo in Quechua. It is a creeper and we usually plant it in our corn fields. Marrows are white and green. We use them to treat fever in sick animals.

BARLEY. *Hordeum Vulgare*. It grows in hot and cold areas. It has great nutritional value and is the staple diet of the poor.
We use the very fine straw as fodder for cattle and horses and the rest as fertilizer.

MAIZE. *Zea Maize*. Sara in Quechua. It has long leaves. The Incas considered it sacred and corn beer was given as offering to the Sun God.
At present we all grow maize and we use it in a variety of dishes.

EGGFRUIT. *Pouteria Lucuma*. Rugma in Quechua. The tree is tall and with very thick foliage, it is a beautiful tree. We use its wood for fine carpentry work. Its fruit is yellow and dry and we use it to make a variety of sweets, it is also used as a cure for diarrhea.

POTATO. *Solarum Tuberosum*. Papa in Quechua They start sowing potatoes in the Highlands in October. Many people sow them on the second of November, the day of the dead, because they believe that potatoes sown on that day will grow the size of a human head.
It is said that potatoes helped to alleviate hunger around the world.

QUINOA. *Chenopodium Quinoa*. Parca in Quechua and supha in Aymara. It grows up to two meters and is one of the main Andean vegetables along with maize and potatoes. Women in my village cook "lawa" quinoa soup. They also prepare "tugra" out of burned quinoa stems which is a substance used by coca chewers to mix with coca leaves. Shamans use it to induce vomit and sweat, also as a laxative and duretic.

PRICKLY PEAR. *Opuntia Ficus-indica*. Tuna in Quechua. There is plenty of them between January and March. We have them in many different colours. They are greatly appreciated in my village. Some of my neighbours eat up to one hundred and fifty prickly pears a day.

It is said that prickly pears and maize talk to each other. The prickly pear tells the maize: "It is your turn to feed our children now, because I have already fed them for three months".

GLOSSARY

Aji   *Capsicum spp.* Chili has been cultivated since pre Inca time, it is a hot condiment. In the Amazone it is used as a dye and as a laxative

Aclla   Chosen woman during the Inca Empire.

Atiy   Power

Amaru   Snake or mythological flying serpent.

Anases   Skunks

Apu   Mountain God. Mountain Peaks worshipped as Gods, who are believed to protect and punish people in their vecinity.

Asangate   Sacred mountain near Cuzco.

Ayahuasca   Hallucinogenic plant, in Quechua means vine of the dead.

Ayllu   Andean clan or kinship group.

Ayni   To borrow, also the Andean system of reciprocal labour exchange.

Brujo   Witch doctor or shaman.

Camote　　　*Ipomoea Batata.* Aje or Apichu in Quechua. Tuctuca in Aymara. Cari in Shipibo. Culiti in Ashanica. Cumala Huasca in Campa. Adauk in Aguaruna. Curiti in Machiguenga. Sweet Potato has been cultivated since 8000 BC and has been found in pre-Inca pottery and tumbs. It is a short plant with plenty of roots. We eat the roots either boiled, roasted or in jam.

Coca Mama　　Inca Coca Goddess.

Conopas　　Small statues carved in stone that represent deities who protect crops and animals. They are shaped as llamas, alpacas, corn, potatoes, etc. and are kept at home or in farm land.

Copacati　　Guardian God of Lake Titicaca

Chasca　　Morning Star. Venus. It also means dishevelled hair

Chasqui　　Messenger during the Inca Epoch.

Chicha　　Popular Andean beer made out of fermented corn, barley or quinoa.

Chihuanco　　*Turdus Chiguanco.* It is a gray bird with a long yellow beak, it measures about twenty seven centimeters. It is found in dry Andean areas.

Guacamayo　　*Psittacidae.* It is a tropical bird which can also be found in the Amazone region. It is the largest known parrot and feeds on fruits, seeds and leaves. It has striking

124

feathers: blue, yellow, red and green. There are fourty nine varieties in Peru alone.

Guanaco   *Lama Guanicoe*. It is a South American cameloid with long neck, its body is covered in wool twelve centimeters long. They are black, gray, white or a combination of these colours. They have not been domesticated on the same scale that lamas have. Their meat is used to prepare many dishes and ropes and leather objects are made out of their skin. They are becoming extint.

Huaca   It is a wide concept in Andean religion. It is a sacred place in nature or a worshipped object or idol. It could be a mountain,a burial place or a rare shaped stone.

Huacapvillac Huaca Interpreter.

Huaychao   A province in Ayacucho Department, Peru.

Inti Raymi   Sun festival celebrated during the Summer Solstice in Cuzco.

Illapa   God of thunder and lightening.

Isango   A very small mite which attacks the lower layer of the skin in human beings, pigs, hens, etc. We are only aware of it through the swellings it produces.

Kay Pacha   Earth.

Laycca   Female Healer.

Masato   The most popular drink in the Amazone. It is made out of fermented cassava.

Mashuas   *Tropaeolum Tuberosum*. A herb with compact foilage. Its roots look like potatoes between five and fifteen centimeters long, which might be white, yellow and orange. It has been cultivated since pre-hispanic time and its image has been found in ancient pottery. Its roots, flowers andnew leaves are edible. Shamans use it to get rid of kidney stones and to cure urinary problems, as well as, an antibiotic. It is said that lowers the level of testosterone, reducing sexual desire.

Oca   *Oxalis Tuberosa*. It grows up to twnty to thirty centimeters high, has suculent stems and yellow flowers with five petals. Its tubers are five to fifteen centimeters long and they are eaten only after having been sun dried over a few days to increse its sacarine content. Their nutritional value is the same as potatoes'.

Ollucos   *Ullucus Tuberosus*. it is a short plant with suculent and slimy stems. Its roots are eaten in various dishes. Shamans use it to help with child birth; to cure stomach pain; headaches; tumours and mild dermatitis.

Otorongo   *Pantera Onca*. It is the biggest feline in America. In Quechua means the one who kills while it jumps. The Incas carried its effigy in their battles.

Pacarina   Place where the first ancestor of the kinship group is said to have appeared.

Quechua   It means people's language. It was the Inca Empire's official language. It is the second most spoken language in South America today, followed by Aymara and Guarani.

Sajino   *Tayassu Tajano.* It is a large rodent mammal and is the most widespread spieces in the Amazone.

Tanka   *Mazama Chunyi.* It is a mammal and lives in the Andes and the High Amazone jungle. Its loud shriks can be heard from far away.

Tamamuri   It is a large Amazonian tree, it is sought after for its wood and shamans use it to cure rheumatism and venereal deseases.

Tawantinsuyo Inca Empire. Literally means four regions.

Tumi   Knife used in ritual sacrifices.

Vizcacha   A type of brown rabbit from the Andes.

Yuca   *Manihot esculenta.* Rumo in Quechua. Atsa in Shipibo. Canari in Ashanica and Secachi in Machiguenga. It is a bush that grows up to three meters high. Its roots are edible and shamans use its boilded leaves to cure skin deseases, burns and measles, as well as, to alliviate diarrhoea.

BIBLIOGRAFÍA

Avila, Francisco de

Ritos y Tradiciones de Huarochirí, IFEA, Lima 1999

Espinoza Soriano, Waldemar

Los Incas: Economía, Sociedad y Estado en la era del Tahuantinsuyo. Amaru Editores, Lima, 1987.

Gonzáles Vigil, Ricardo

El cuento Peruano 1980 1989, Ediciones Copé, Lima, 1997

Kauffmann, Federico

Manual de Arqueología Peruana. 6ta. Edición Ediciones Peisa, Lima, 1978.

Macera, Pablo

Flora y Fauna de Sarhua. Edición de la Universidad Nacional Mayor de San Marcos, Lima 1999.

Morote Best, Efrain

Aldeas Sumergidas: Cultura Popular y Sociedad en los Andes, Ediciones CBC, Cuzco, 1988.

Porras Barrenechea, Raúl

Mito, Tradición e Historia del Perú. Tomo II Ediciones Peisa, Lima, 1974.

Rostworowski, María

Etnia y Sociedad, Costa Peruana Prehispánica, IEP, Lima, 1977.

Recursos Naturales, Renovables y Pesca. Siglos XVI y XVII. IEP, Lima. 1981
Estructuras Andinas de Poder. Ideología Religiosa y Política. 4ta. edición. IEP, Lima, 1996.

Pachacamac y el Señor de los
Milagros. Una Trayectoria
Milenaria. IEP, Lima, 1992

Santa Cruz Pachacuti, Juan   Relación de antigüedades de este
Reino del Perú,
Fondo de Cultura Económica,
Lima, 1995.

Toro Montalvo, César   Mitos y Leyendas del Perú. AFA
Editores, 1990, Lima, 3 Tomos.

Valcárcel, Luis E.   Etnohistoria del Perú Antiguo,
UNMSM, Lima, 1967

Zuidema, R. Tom   Mito e Historia en el Antiguo
Perú "Allpanchis" Nro. 10,
Cuzco, 1977.